KU-374-027

Plymouth
~DEVON~

CAP'N JASPERS

THE VOYAGE OF THE ARCTIC TERN

To Muriel

Hope you tolerate this : the next edition is a
(the lighter than this one ~ which was self published. —
Not quite up to "Munroe" standard, perhaps. —
But --
       Best wishes
            Hugh

Tern Tale

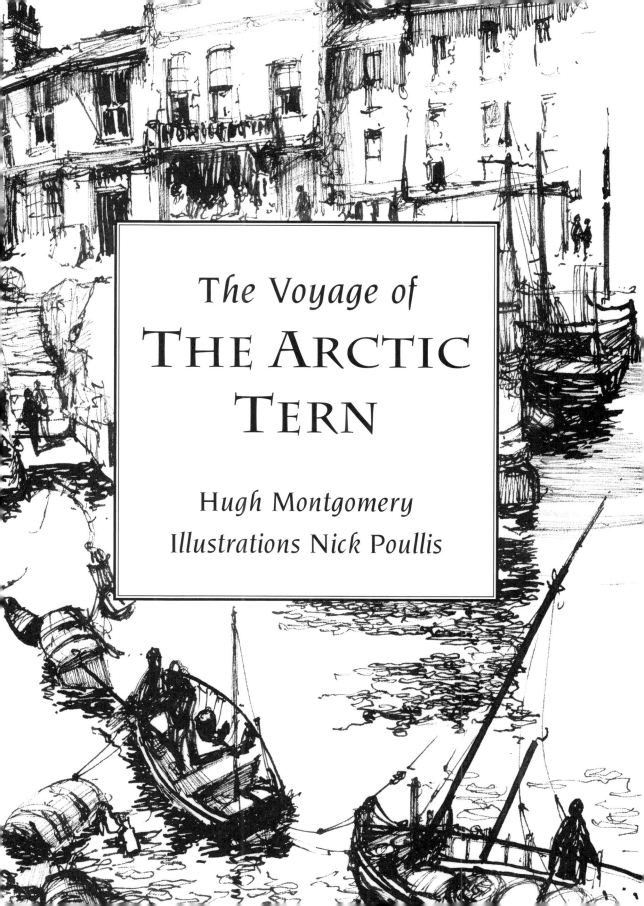

The Voyage of
THE ARCTIC TERN

Hugh Montgomery

Illustrations Nick Poullis

First published in Great Britain in 2000
by Synapse·GB Limited
Monks Brook House
13-17 Hursley Road
Chandlers Ford
Hampshire SO53 2FW

Copyright © 2000 Hugh Montgomery (text)
© 2000 Nick Poullis (illustrations)

The author asserts his moral right to be identified as the
author of the work in relation to all such rights as are
granted by the Author to the Publisher under the UK
Copyright, Designs and Patents Act 1988.

All rights reserved. No part of this publication may be
reproduced, stored in a retrieval system, or transmitted in
any form or by any means, electronic, mechanical, photo-
copying, recording or otherwise, without the prior
written permission of the copyright owners.

ISBN 0-9539159-0-5

Produced by Interimage
2 Butlers Close
Amersham
Bucks HP6 5PY

Editor Miriam Richardson
Design Mónica Bratt

Printed and bound in Great Britain
by Butler & Tanner
Frome
England

Foreword

SOMETIMES THE UNEXPECTED happens, and in the modern world where the exciting years of childhood seem to be dominated by computer games, a new book arrives which delights the heart and the mind.

The Voyage of the Arctic Tern is an epic tale of sailing ships and sailors. It bristles with avarice, sunken treasure and treachery, but good men triumph and bad men are exposed as base and worthless. Tales like this occur throughout history and they have been told over the centuries in many languages and by people of very different backgrounds. It is the author's use of lyrical verse to tell the tale three ways at three different periods of our maritime history that sets this book apart.

This beautiful, descriptive narrative and the outstanding illustrations by Nick Poullis open the imagination and bring back memories to those of us who use the sea as our workshop. I hope it will encourage many young readers to understand and love the sea and sailing ships. Then perhaps they will dream a few dreams and, like the author, they will go on to explore the wonderful world beneath the sea for themselves.

Mrs Margaret Rule, CBE FSA

One more moonrise. One less sunset. Rhythmic comforts, like the tides
Familiar hand-sweep on skies clockface, pacing out our passing lives.
But cursed to live while others die, an anguished sailor finds no peace,
Each lunar tick just marking time. Until forgiveness brings release.

BOOK ONE

THE

PRESENT

DAY

I
PLYMOUTH

IN DEVON LIES the Naval Town of Plymouth,
The home of submarines and ships of war,
Of frigates, battleships and pleasure cruisers,
Of ferries, cargo boats and many more.
In summer, tourists throng along the sea front
Or splash along the beach at Bovisand
Or climb the Mayflower steps where Pilgrim Fathers
Set sail to colonise a foreign land.

But when you visit, try to look about you,
Beyond the burgers, ice-cream and the trips:
Imagine what this place might once have looked like
When Plymouth Sound was full of wooden ships.
The ancient port would then be full of dangers:
Of vagabonds and smugglers – pirates too,
And simply walking out alone one evening
Could find you coming round as press-ganged crew.

In any case, it seeps like milk
Along the inky ocean floor.
In half an hour, or maybe less,
It's crossed the Sound and reached the shore.
And to the Barbican it comes:
The temperature begins to fall
As tongues of mist lick seafront stones
And clammy fog spills o'er the wall.

And rising up, great rolling banks
Will spill and tumble, start to set.
Pale haloes form around the lights
And cobbles bathe in ice-cold sweat.
On silence, muffled sounds intrude –
The creak of timbers. Bilge's slop.
The lonely whale-song sound of fog-horns.
Licking water's slap and drop.

And from the mist appear twelve ships
Each sailing in the wake before.
They make their way to Sutton Pool
Then moor to rings upon the shore.
And from each boat, a fisherman
Steps out and walks along the side
And makes his way along the front.
Seeks "The Admiral McBride".

The pub itself is quite deserted:
No-one comes to drink this night
Nor dares to walk the cobbled streets –
And no-one will until first light.
The doors will all be locked securely –
Shutters up, all curtains drawn,
All children banished to their beds
Where each shall stay until the dawn.

Inside the pub a table stands
With thirteen places, thirteen chairs.
And by each seat, a place is set
And at each place, a meal prepared.
Each has an ancient china plate
And each a frothing pint of beer
And on each plate some black rye-bread –
The meal identical each year.

These twelve men take their silent places,
Rise as one and turn to face
The empty chair which heads the table:
One man missing from his place.
Now solemnly they take their drinks:
In foreign tongue they make a toast:
Raise glasses to an absent friend:
"The memory of Bruno's ghost!"

For some time now they sit and talk
Of fearsome days and nights long past,
Of howling winds and heaving seas
And days of toil beneath the mast.
And by tradition, tell the story
– One of which you soon will learn –
Of treason, treachery and treasure
. . . Voyages on *The Arctic Tern*.

They leave the building some time later
Bolt the door, and turn the key,
Retrace their steps and board their boats
Then silently slip out to sea.
Behind, they leave the room deserted –
Bruno's table-place still set.
His chair still drawn. Plate undisturbed.
His bread and beer untouched, as yet . . .

III
THE NEXT MORNING

NOW IN THE MORNING, those that come
Will find those battered trawlers gone.
The fog will clear, the frost will melt
And all that aching tension felt
Throughout the night (in fact for days)
Will dissipate just as the haze.
Doors and curtains open wide
In houses by the waterside
And fisher folk will meet and greet
And natter on the cobbled streets,
Relieved to shed that nameless fear
Until the winter of next year.

As early sunrays seek the frames
And push their way through grimy panes,
So bars and bands and chinks of light
Pick out the places where, last night
Those dozen sailors met to toast
The memory of Bruno's ghost.
And as they pierce the dusty air
The rays light up that thirteenth chair –
The seat which, just like all the rest
Had sat before a pint of best
And, as I have already said,
A single slice of black rye-bread.

But all is not as it had been –
Quite different is the morning scene.
Consumed is Bruno's fine repast:
A foam of ale runs down the glass.
The meal has gone. All that remains
Are crumbs. A crust. A beer-glass stain . . .

Seen trailing from the bolted door
Wet footprints mark the oaken floor.
They lead directly to the chair.
Some salt and sand collected there
Suggests perhaps he sat awhile
To eat the bread and sup his ale.
From there the prints, seen clearly still
Have made their way towards the till
Upon the top of which is left
A token for his beer and rest:
Upon an ancient china plate
A Spanish silver "Piece of Eight".

The barman – you will learn his name –
For many years has been the same.
How long this is, no-one seems sure –
But must be thirty years or more.
This fellow, later in the day,
Collects that silver – not as pay,
But places it behind the bar
Inside an ancient stoneware jar,
Wherein it joins some thirty more,
Collected over years before.

Should someone suffer failing health
Or lose their sight, or lose their wealth;
Lose self-esteem, their will to live
Or feel life's nothing left to give,
Then often they'll suppress their pride,
Seek out "The Admiral McBride"
And leave a note pinned on the door
– So plead the weak, the sick, the poor.
And to those souls, or so they say
Will come a silver coin that day
Each taken from inside that jar
Which lies, in turn, behind that bar.

But what a mystery is this
Whose tokens bring such happiness:
As often as this jar brings cheer
(Which may be many times each year)
The level in the jar won't fall –
In fact, it never drops at all.

To understand such acts as these
You have to cross time's stormy seas
And see a boat moored far away
And watch gold loaded one fine day
So climb aboard, come sail with me
We'll travel through the centuries
And in Seville, in Spain, we'll land
Where treachery is close at hand . . .

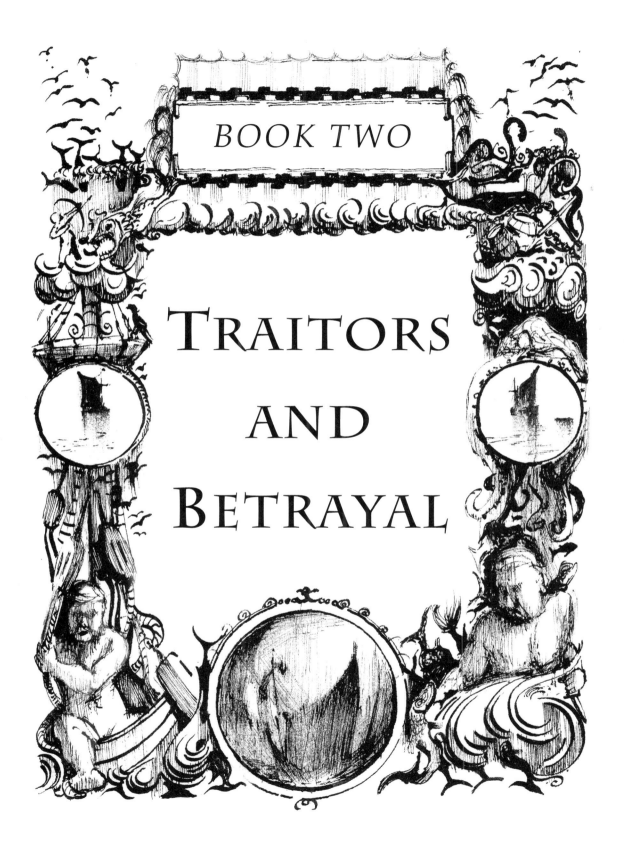

BOOK TWO

TRAITORS
AND
BETRAYAL

Through Spanish seas our way is made
To save the life of one betrayed.

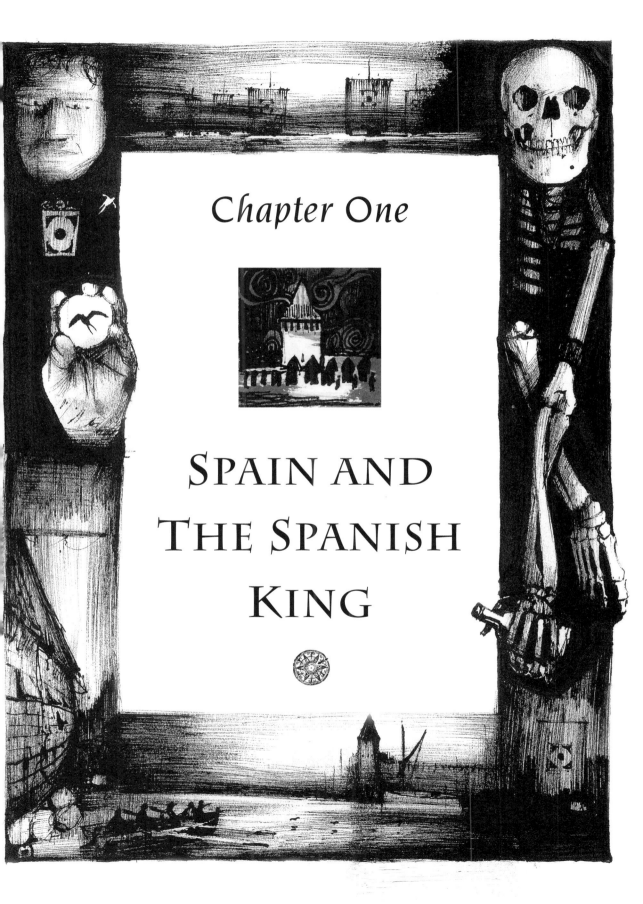

Chapter One

SPAIN AND
THE SPANISH
KING

I
SEVILLE

SUNLIGHT SHATTERS off the sea
And warm winds waft around a host
Of palm trees, nodding as they stand
Like pensioners along the coast.
Tangy smells of Spanish orange
Lift from fruit trees just inland
Which drift and shimmer in the heat
As if afloat in seas of sand.

Traders on Seville's old seafront
Stack their stalls with scents and spice:
With crafted gold or silk in rolls,
And as they work, they shout their price.
Today is just like any other
If you've come to sell and buy,
But in the castle on the hill
Another picture meets the eye.

The servants in the castle weep.
No brightly coloured flags are flown.
The sentries stoop and shake their heads.
The gates are locked. Portcullis down.
For though the walls are eight feet thick
And carved in blocks of solid stone
Still death has made its way inside
And stalked their king upon his throne.

They loved their king. It hurt them so
To see him suffer in this way
And clearly, barring miracles,
He'd not survive another day.
They didn't know, but fighting death
The king stood little chance to win
For none of them had recognised
The enemy who lurked within.

In life, we find two groups of men:
Some dare not trust, try to defend
Themselves from everyone they meet –
See enemies in all their friends.
The other group are noble sorts –
Seek good in everyone they see.
Their trusting nature often leads
To dangerous gullibility.

Now on the whole, there's little doubt:
Contentment comes to those who live
An honest life without mistrust,
Who rarely take, but often give.
But oh! The pain which comes to them
When friends are enemies disguised.
With trust betrayed, and no defence,
They risk their all. May lose their lives.

Such was the source of all the pain
Which filled the castle on this day.
The trusting king, a man of peace
Was dying, having been betrayed.
But often fate will intervene
To damn the wrong, support the right,
Protect the righteous even when
It seems that they have lost the fight . . .

II
MORGAN

A RICH MAN called Morgan was known to the people
But views of him differed with whom you might ask.
Both nobles and courtiers thought of him highly
(Opinions coloured by "gifts" in oak casks).
But ask those who laboured all day on the sea
What they thought of the man, and of what else they'd learned,
And they'd tell of a smuggler, a killer and cheat,
Whose nickname of "Mad Dog" was truly well earned.

He owned half Seville, and a fleet of old ships
Which he used for importing his silver and gold.
But mixed with the jewellery (whose carriage was legal)
Were other more lucrative cargoes he sold.
He smuggled all manner of drink and tobacco
Defending this trade with an uncontrolled wrath.
Should anyone else dare compete in such deals
Well – he'd not stop at killing such men in his path.

On land he was dressed in a way almost formal.
At sea he'd discard all this fashion and charm –
Wear a blue pirate's tunic and razor-sharp cutlass:
A parrot (called Dolly) was perched on one arm.
His herald (embroidered in gold on the pockets
And also on pennants he raised to the skies)
Spoke of stealth and of strength and of far-reaching powers:
T'was an octopus glaring with fiery red eyes.

For his sport, he would sail down the coast for a day
And would climb to the crow's nest, and there he would stand
With his telescope, scanning the distant horizon
And searching the inlets and bays of the land.
When he sighted a ship, he would swing to the helm
And would head for that vessel, and shout to the crew
Who would take down the fiery-eyed octopus emblem:
A black skull and crossbones the flag they then flew.

Having seized all their cargo, he'd muster the men
And insist that they watched as the torched vessel sank.
Completing his pleasure, he'd keel-haul the captain
And make all the rest of their crew walk the plank.
There were thus no survivors to tarnish his image.
Karina, his wife, would not ever suspect
That the 'gentleman merchant' was really a thief
Who would stand at the wheel on a pirate ship's deck.

But unknown to Morgan, there was one survivor –
An Admiral, Hunter, who'd slipped from his grasp.
When he'd captured the ship, Morgan tied up the man
And then hurled him with glee from the top of the mast.
He never resurfaced, so Morgan assumed
That the fall must have stunned him, and caused him to drown,
Whilst in fact far below Hunter fought himself free
Of the ropes and the sacking with which he was bound.

He had floated on currents for almost two days
(And from sunstroke and thirst might have easily died)
When a ship sailing past him caught sight of his body.
They lifted him carefully over the side.
Old Bruno, the captain, was kind to poor Hunter
Shared food and his clothing, went out of his way
To get him back home to his wife in North England –
A debt which Lord Hunter would one day repay.

III
THE SPANISH KING

THE KING was a kind man, a fine man of honour
A man who would always try hard to do good.
He cared for the weak and supported the needy.
He sought to win friends and make peace if he could.
The people adored him, admired him and honoured him.
Merchants lived happily, safe and secure
Giving part of their earnings in tax as he asked them:
Happy to see how he tended the poor.

But some men were greedy, despising the king
And resenting the taxes he put on their wealth:
Convinced they should fight and in war win more riches
And spend not one coin on the sick or their health.
Morgan was one man of such a persuasion:
Begrudging each dollar of tax that was spent.
He was shrewd though, pretending to honour the king,
Who thus never suspected his deep discontent.

As time passed this loathing became an obsession.
With friends, who would never report what he said,
He would mutter and curse, say they'd all do much better
If sickness should strike and the king end up dead!
Consumed with such bitterness, Mad Morgan plotted.
He'd work for the poor, make his loyalty known.
But once in a post above any suspicion,
He'd poison the king and himself take the throne.

In only a year he became Chief Advisor.
His views on all matters were frequently sought.
The king came to value his judgement most highly.
He soon was in favour with all in the court.
He tended the servants, and treated them kindly:
He increased their wages, and won them as friends.
Of course, he did not really like them at all –
His control of the court was a means to an end.

Each morning, the personal cook to the king
Would rise early and make his way down to the shore
Where he'd purchase the best of the fish and the produce
And carry it back to the kitchen and store.
It was therefore most odd when the cook left one morning
And hadn't returned by the end of the day.
It would seem that he must have run off with the money
(At least, that's what Morgan was soon heard to say.).

It was now Morgan's job to employ a new cook
Which he managed to do in a very short time.
It is odd no-one thought to inquire where he'd come from,
Or why he should bring a supply of sweet wine.
A man who had lived through the pirates' attack
(And I've told you that Hunter was one of the few)
Would have known that the man who now cooked for the king
Had in fact been the cook on the pirate ship too.

A little while later, the king became ill.
He grew sicker and weaker with each passing day,
And with headaches and cramps, he'd eat scarcely a morsel –
It seemed to them all he would soon pass away . . .
A doctor was called, who declared himself baffled:
Unable to diagnose what had gone wrong.
With leeches and potions, he hoped for a cure,
Though the king, he suspected, would not last for long.

As the illness progressed, it would often be noted
How Morgan would come, thinking nothing of time
And would sit by the bedside and tend him for hours:
Would moisten his lips with that sweet-tasting wine.
The king was most grateful, astonished that Morgan
Should humble himself in the role of a nurse:
Found comfort in drinking the wine that he brought
Though he noticed that, soon, he would feel strangely worse.

The monarch knew well that his life would soon end
And was keen that his heir should be heard as a voice
Of compassion, integrity, love and of honour.
His advisor was clearly the obvious choice.
The king called his council, announced his decision:
To Morgan, his friend and advisor, he'd hand
All the burdens of ruling the whole Spanish Empire:
Of protecting both rich and the poor in the land.

Just as Morgan had planned, then, events had unfolded:
The throne, he felt sure, would be his on that day.
He could not have foreseen, though, the card fate would deal him
By way of a boat which arrived in the bay.

Chapter Two

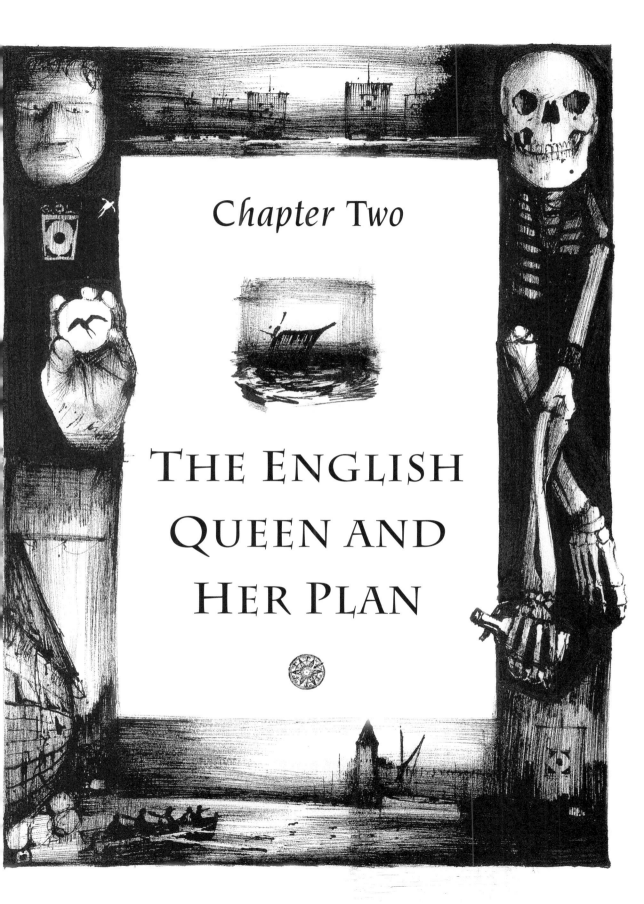

THE ENGLISH QUEEN AND HER PLAN

I
THE QUEEN AND LORD HUNTER

IN LONDON, in that very year
(The day the cook had disappeared:
As Mad Dog Morgan sought to reign
By killing off the king of Spain)
The English Queen called to her court
The councillors and aides she thought
Might guide her as she tried to make
Her peace with other heads of state.

The English navy long had sought
To rule the waves, and each year fought
To sink the ships of other powers
And keep the trade routes ever ours.
This violent conquest by the sword
Brought untold riches from abroad
With all the wealth of other lands
Delivered into English hands.

Thus, many men would not support
These plans for peace when they had brought
Vast wealth and booty – massive hoards
Of gold and silver – from abroad.
A change to peaceful policy
Could make these men sworn enemies.
So any such diplomacy
Would need the utmost secrecy.

The Queen thus to her meeting called
The man she trusted most of all.
From Durham, then, Lord Hunter came
To be her messenger to Spain.
Now admiral of all her fleet,
She knew that he would be discreet
And not reveal her secret plan
To any other Englishman.

She asked that he should seek a crew
Of men he trusted through and through
To never breathe a single word
To anyone of what they'd heard:
A crew who'd brave the stormy seas
And bear her message loyally.
To Spain would stretch an English hand
To offer peace between two lands.

Lord Hunter heard what she proposed
Then, without question, he arose.
He bowed, and swore an oath that he
Would bear her message faithfully.
He took the scroll which she proffered
And left the room without a word.
"Godspeed," she called, "and understand:
Our hopes of peace lie in your hands."

II
LOUISE AND
LORD HUNTER

A WOMAN (LOUISE) and her father were waiting
In Durham for Hunter, who'd said he'd return.
He saddled his horse, and at once left to see her:
He'd given his word and would not let her down.
'Midst stormclouds and rain, then, he rode through the night-time
Till wet and bedraggled he came to her home.
She kissed him. At once, she could tell he was troubled
And asked if her father could leave them alone.

He knew time was short, that his life was at risk
From the perilous trip and the men he would cross:
In both Spain and England, some merchants made money
From warfare: to these, any peace would mean loss.
He'd promised the Queen that he'd keep the plan secret:
That no-one would hear what she'd asked him to do.
Louise, though, had promised she'd never betray him
And he, in his turn, had sworn honesty too.

He wept as he told her that now he must leave her:
He couldn't explain why or where he must go.
The chance he might die bore no terror at all:
The fact they were parting hurt more than she'd know.
He wished to make certain that, if fate decreed it
And death should befall him, the goods that he owned
Would be passed to the woman he loved above all:
That Louise would inherit his lands and his home.

If married, he said, they would be strong together.
In spirit, they'd always be one from that day.
She'd know that his thoughts would be constantly with her
No matter how long he remained far away.
In practical terms, she would share his belongings,
Own half of his chattels, and half of his land.
At least, should he die, he would know she'd be cared for.
He knelt as he begged her to offer her hand.

For a while she said nothing, but walked off alone
As she thought of his offer, and what she should do.
She knew she would love him wherever he went,
And she knew, to that love, she would ever be true.
This wedding day, then, would be what she had yearned for
(She'd long dreamed of spending her life by his side)
But his leaving would make the day sad beyond measure.
She walked back to face him, and then she replied.

"I don't wish to know why it is you must leave me
Nor hear of the perils that threaten your life.
You know, though, I'll wait here until your return
And promise that then you shall make me your wife.
You'll not do so now, for the joy it would bring
Would be marred by the fact that we'd soon have to part.
Instead, let us wait for that day in the future
When marriage will mark not an end – but a start!"

"Godspeed, then, my Lord. May your journey be safe.
May you guard your own life as you'd surely guard mine.
Try to think of me daily at sunrise and sunset
For prayers shall I send you each day at these times.
If ever you're threatened, or fear for your life –
At such times as you're scared, when you feel you're alone –
Then think of my name, and I'll come to your rescue –
I'll send you a guide who will bring you back home."

He packed, then, in sorrow and left her next morning,
And rode off to Plymouth in search of a crew
And a ship that would carry him safely to Spain
And could carry him back to his native shores too.
Now only one man in the whole of the country
He trusted enough to enlist in this task:
'Twas the man who had once saved his life far away.
It was Bruno, the captain, he knew he must ask.

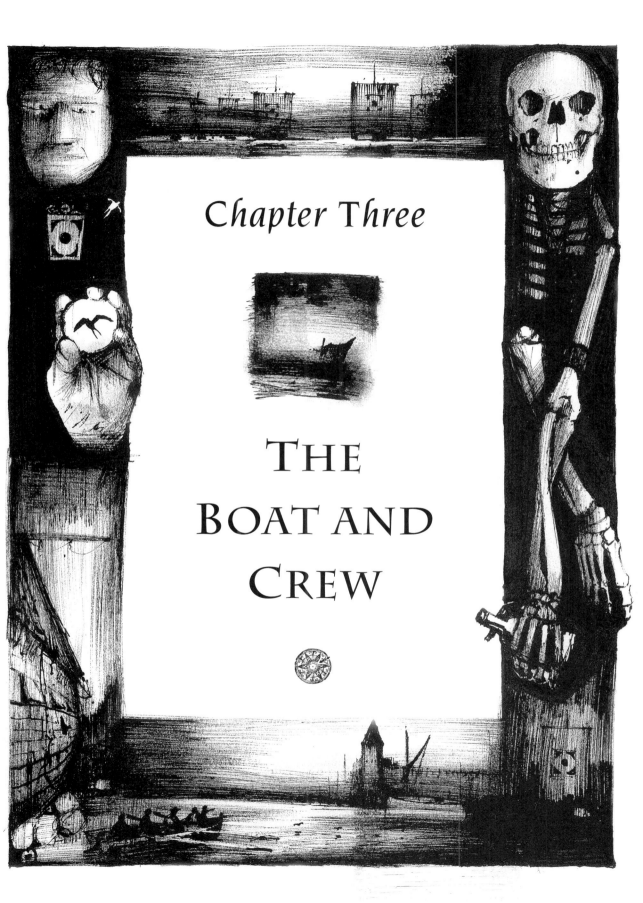

Chapter Three

THE
BOAT AND
CREW

I

THE ARCTIC TERN

STRANGE TO TELL, but no-one knew just when the ship was made.
Her timbers, burned by sun and salt, seemed of a different age.
The old men claimed, as children, that they'd seen her, and would tell
How every generation past remembered her as well.

They also noted, strangely, that she'd sailed through violent seas
But never once was seen to suffer any injury.
And after howling storms, they'd see her moored up by the wall.
With boats wrecked all around her, she'd have not one scratch at all.

At forty feet, it seemed that she was far too small to brave
The minor coastal inlets, let alone vast ocean waves.
The ignorant dismissed her, for they never would have thought
That though she'd go to sea for months, she'd not once sail to port.

The clinker hull had darkened through the years of salty spray.
The wheel house matched its colour, and the ageing sails were grey.
And if you looked quite closely, gazing up towards the prow
A tiny bird with wings spread wide was painted on her bow.

Her name, *The Arctic Tern*, was seen inscribed beside the bird.
The locals didn't bother now considering the words,
For what, or where, "The Arctic" was in those days wasn't known
(In fact, the icy wastelands were not found for years to come).

Her captain also puzzled them: when questioned, they would frown
And say it seemed forever that he'd lived here in the town.
He hadn't aged at all, they said, so far as they could see,
And generations past had seen him putting out to sea.

Remember how I told you that a pirate ship, one day
Had sunk a boat and drowned the crew in waters far away?
And how it was that Hunter had escaped the pirate grasp
And lived to tell the tale of how he'd tumbled from the mast?

Remember how he'd drifted, and how certain you can be
That he'd have died of thirst, or drowned, if not plucked from the sea?
Well, Bruno was that saviour who had plucked him from the foam:
The Arctic Tern the vessel which had carried him back home.

Lord Hunter thus decided that to reach the Spanish Port
He'd need to find a captain – it was Bruno that he sought.
So now you know about her and can see her, bow to stern
I'll tell you of the captain of that ship, *The Arctic Tern*.

II
BRUNO THE CAPTAIN

BRUNO WAS ALWAYS a loner, they said,
But if sought he could often be found at low tide
In a Barbican pub he'd frequented for years –
Took its name from the Admiral known as "McBride".
He would walk from his boat in his old leather boots,
And the barman would say that the man, without fail,
Would leave pools of salt water and sand from his feet
From the door to his seat in an unsightly trail.

A creature of habit, his meals were the same –
for his lunch and his supper, black rye-bread he ate.
A pint of best bitter would help him wash down
Each and every last morsel that lay on his plate.
He would sit in the corner, and sipping his ale
He would nod to the barman as each pint was sent.
He'd say not a word, but would think private thoughts
And would watch as the fishermen came, drank and went.

All that he did, he would do the same way.
Though the reason for this no-one there could decide.
He would take off his jacket and, folding the sleeves,
He would lay it out flat on the floor by his side.
Whatever was served him (no matter how much)
He would finish completely – leave nothing to show
For a full plate of food, or a bottle of rum,
For he'd finish each morsel before he would go.

His face had been tanned, such that no-one could gauge
What his race or his natural colour had been,
While an old captain's hat (which he rarely removed)
Meant his hair (what was left of it!) wasn't much seen.
A furrowed dark brow made him constantly thoughtful.
His eyes, though, were burning like fiery hot coals
So that those who by chance might have glanced at them briefly
Would feel that he'd glimpsed what lay deep in their souls.

A black tangled beard, caked in decades of sea salt,
Had spilled from his chin in an unruly pile.
In the midst of this mass lay expressionless lips
For the hair on his head was as thin as his smile.
But somehow one felt that this man was a friend:
That he'd help anyone who he found in distress
And indeed, there were many who spoke of his acts
Of humility, sacrifice and of largesse.

Not many were counted as friends of Old Bruno.
Though those that had known him for years often tried
To engage him in talk of his life and adventures,
He'd never been known to respond or confide.
There *were* one or two, though, it seemed that he trusted:
With them he'd be seen to converse in hushed tones.
These men were the sort who could keep their own counsel –
Who didn't need company more than their own.

III
BRUNO'S FRIENDS:
ADRIAN THE BARMAN

THE FIRST OF THESE folk was the pub cook and barman.
Though many a customer likes a good chat,
These two seemed more earnest when talking together:
A bond seemed to bind them more deeply than that.
In fact, it was said by the elderly locals
That Adrian had, in the past sailed as crew:
That *The Arctic Tern* left for those long months at sea
not with Bruno alone, but with Adrian too.

A family man, he worked hard to support
Both a wife and two children, with each penny sent
Back to Bridget, his wife, and to sons Jack and Paddy
Who lived in his parents' home somewhere in Kent.
The pittance he kept was not spent on high living
But saved in an earthenware pot at the bar
So his family, one day, could come down and live
In a house he would pay for with coins from the jar.

He cherished the hope that one day he might run
His own pub, where he'd serve not just beer but fine food.
The public would know what a great cook he was:
They'd hail him, and say to him, "Well! That *was* good !"
His customers teased him about his ambitions
And so did his friends. "I suspect," said his wife,
"That although in the future your dreams may come true,
We may well have to wait here until the next life!"

The reason she laughed at his plans for a business
Were clear, for each person who knew him agreed
That his heart was as big as the seas that he'd sailed,
And he'd always give money to those found in need.
In fact, those in trouble all knew what to do
And might secretly come to his doorway by night,
Leaving on it a note which would speak of their anguish.
Next day they'd find coins which would help ease their plight.

When Bruno would later be asked by Lord Hunter
To carry him safely to far Spanish shores
He would look for some crewmen to come on the voyage
And would think of the men who'd gone with him before.
And so it would be that Old Bruno would ask him
To pack up his things and get ready to go.
As *The Arctic Tern* sailed, he'd be found in the galley
Preparing the food as the ship's cook below.

IV
BRUNO'S FRIENDS: DOCTOR CHRIS

THERE WAS ONE MORE man who'd sailed with him before,
Who in years past had solemnly given his pledge
That with Bruno he'd travel again, should he ask:
A doctor of medicine, his name was Chris Edge.
He claimed that diseases were oft caused by creatures
Whose minuscule size made them hard to detect.
He was mocked (though his notes were one day read in France
By a fellow called Pasteur, who proved him correct.)

His other great passion (for things that were poisonous)
Began in his childhood when, walking one day
He consumed some wild berries, and soon became ill
And was lucky that night he did not pass away.
He prided himself that there wasn't a man
Who knew more about toxins than he himself knew.
He'd tell at a glance if a man had been poisoned:
Say when it was done, and with what substance too.

He now lived in Oxford with Jenny his wife
Who had recently studied the silversmith's art.
The brooches and rings she now fashioned at home
Were much sought by the wealthy in near and far parts.
Her finest creation, in silver and gold,
Showed the heads of her daughters, with one on each side.
Victoria, next to her sib Alexandra,
Gazed out from a brooch which she wore with great pride.

The first year he'd known her, Chris left for a voyage
With Old Bruno, and stayed for some months overseas.
Returning, he said that they'd sailed to the East,
That he'd brought her some gifts which he called "Bonsai Trees".
She tended them well, though she feared some might say
It was witchcraft she practised to make sure each stayed
Just a few inches high from the roots to the tip:
From all but her children, she hid them away.

So this was the man who, when summoned by Bruno,
Would hurry to Plymouth, avoiding delay,
To meet once again with his sailing companions,
And hear what Lord Hunter himself had to say.
He knew that the trip would be one of importance:
A meeting was planned at which much was at stake.
His wife sent him off with the brooch that she wore
And a fine Bonsai tree, as two gifts he could take.

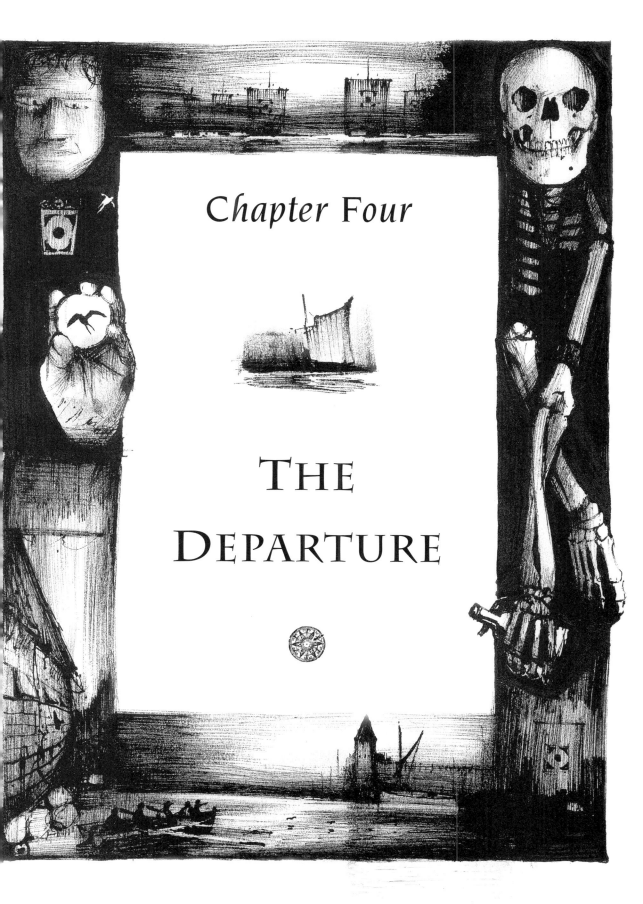

Chapter Four

THE

DEPARTURE

I
LORD HUNTER ARRIVES

THE LONG RIDE FROM Durham left Hunter exhausted,
But still he endeavoured, on reaching the port,
To seek his friend Bruno who knew he was coming
(He'd first sent a message when at the Queen's court).
He stabled his horse in a place close to Greenbank,
But first let it drink from a trough close to hand.
(If you walk there today you can find this same place
For the trough, carved in granite, is one that still stands).

He walked down the hill and then on through a crossroads
Where now stands a church which was bombed in the war.
Then on to the seafront, across the stone cobbles
(The same ones you'll note which I've mentioned before.)
Along the cold streets, past the rings to which vessels
Could tie themselves safely and lie until light:
(The ones that I'd mentioned, which twelve ghostly vessels
Would moor to, each year, on a cold winter's night.

He entered the pub, and at once saw his friend
Who was sitting, as normal, away from the door:
His jacket removed, with the sleeves neatly folded
Was laid out, by habit, beside on the floor.
How strange, though, that Bruno should seem to have known
Just precisely when Hunter would choose to arrive:
Not minutes before, he had called to the barman
"A pint for my guest". It now stood to one side.

They sat there that evening and talked of old times,
Recollecting the details of just how, one day
Bruno rescued Lord Hunter from imminent death
As he floated alone in a sea far away.
It seemed, though, that Bruno would take little credit
for lifting him out, and for taking him home.
"Once I knew of your plight, could I ever have stayed?
If it wasn't for you, I would never have gone."

These words were surprising to Hunter, who thought
His discovery purely a matter of chance.
The rescue was not due to planning, he thought,
And owed nothing to choice, but to pure circumstance.
Besides, it defied any logic at all
To consider that Bruno could ever foretell
The events which befell him at Morgan's cruel hand,
To predict what would happen, and quite where as well.

Nonetheless, in the past he had had his suspicions:
In Plymouth, before, he had heard others talk
Of the strange way that Bruno would suddenly choose
To make ready his vessel and sail from the port;
How often such journeys would happen to take him
To places where others might suffer duress –
As if, so they said, he was doing a job
And was called to these missions by sensing distress.

It was midnight when all of the people had gone
With Lord Hunter and Bruno the ones left behind.
Having served the last customer, Adrian joined them.
Together they shared in a jug of mulled wine.
They talked very little, content in the silence
Which only close friends ever share in this way
Leaving talk of their mission till Chris Edge arrived –
He would be there, most likely, within a few days.

By two in the morning, on reaching his lodgings,
Lord Hunter could finally fall into bed.
He'd rushed to the Queen, to Louise then to Plymouth:
Completely exhausted, he slept like the dead.
His dreams were confusing, with pictures of Plymouth,
Of coastlines and palm trees and grapes on the vine:
And of pirates and kings, and an octopus glaring.
And also of bottles of sweet tasting wine . . .

II
CHRIS EDGE ARRIVES

HE WOKE THE NEXT morning to noise from the courtyard –
A carriage, it seemed, had drawn up just outside.
From sounds that he heard and the things that were said,
It appeared that not long ago Chris had arrived.
So Lord Hunter arose and went out to the doctor
And greeted him warmly, explaining that he
Was the man who had asked for Old Bruno's assistance,
And one of the group who would soon put to sea.

They walked to the Barbican, went to the quay
Where the trawlers each morning unloaded, and where
Captain Jasper (a man now too old to set sail)
Cooked them fish, freshly caught, on a stall he had there.
Round the corner, at Jago's, crisp loaves from the oven
Exuded sweet smells as they cooled on a tray.
Even now, "Cap'n Jasper's" still stands by the market:
The baker's shop, too, you can find to this day.

On the way back, they walked to the pub and left word
For the barman that Chris had now safely arrived.
Together, they walked to their lodgings in Greenbank
Going up from the quay and along Bretonside.
The rest of the day they spent sorting possessions,
And packing those things which they'd load on the ship.
This was all done in secret, lest anyone learn
Of the voyage and reasons for making the trip.

III
MEETINGS

I N GREENBANK, that evening, a carriage arrived
Bearing Adrian, Bruno, and one person more:
It was Daisy – a mongrel who lived on the boat,
And whose presence I ought to have mentioned before.
The doctor and barman were friends from past travels:
They'd both sailed with Bruno so now, at first sight,
Hunter ran from the door to the side of the carriage
Whilst Adrian let out a whoop of delight.

The four of them now took their coach through the town.
They rode eastwards through Plymstock, and thus made their way
Past the clifftops at Staddon, and on up the hill
To descend, in the end, down to Bovisand Bay.
Far away from the town, they were able to talk
Of their journey together, without any fear
That by accident someone might catch what they said
(Or worse still, make deliberate efforts to hear.)

They now built a hearth from some rocks which they gathered:
Lit dull sea-stained driftwood they found close at hand.
Young Adrian cooked them a meal in the embers
Which glowed like bright rubies in settings of sand.
When fine food and ale had been finished entirely,
And flickering flames buttered gold on their cheeks,
The three who'd been summoned now sat in a circle
And looked to Lord Hunter, who started to speak.

He told them that decades of war had achieved
Very little but misery, hunger and pain:
That the Queen wanted friendship, an end to the fighting,
And wished above all for a treaty with Spain:
To do this risked angering traders and merchants
Who'd profited, always, from war between lands;
She'd given Lord Hunter a personal message
Addressed to the king, to deliver by hand.

He said that the trip was most certainly dangerous,
And that Adrian ought to give thought to his sons,
For his death would leave Bridget alone with the children:
They'd all understand if he chose not to come.
And Chris should consider his wife and his children:
Should also take heed of the fact that his skills
Were important to all of the patients he treated:
He risked both his own life, and those of the ill.

The trip was a gamble. They might come away
With a treaty which guaranteed peace, on one hand.
On the other, the Spanish might think it a trap
And might kill them, or jail them for years in their land.
Lord Hunter fell silent. The men, too, said nothing.
They thought of the mission which Hunter proposed
And balanced the good which might come to the country
With personal dangers. Then each man arose.

It was no great surprise to Lord Hunter to hear
that each one of them strongly approved of the plan
Whose success, they all felt, was of greater importance
Than dangers of any sort faced by one man.
The longer they waited, the greater the chance
That their presence was questioned, so any delay
Would be best kept as brief as it possibly could.
They agreed to be ready to sail in three days.

At midnight, they met in the pub three days later:
With everything packed, made their way to the quay.
First went Daisy the dog, and behind her went Bruno
With Adrian (carrying pans) number three.
Lord Hunter went next, with the scroll from the Queen
Then Chris Edge (who took with him the old Bonsai tree
And the shining medallion his wife had sent with him).
On board before sunrise, they slipped out to sea . . .

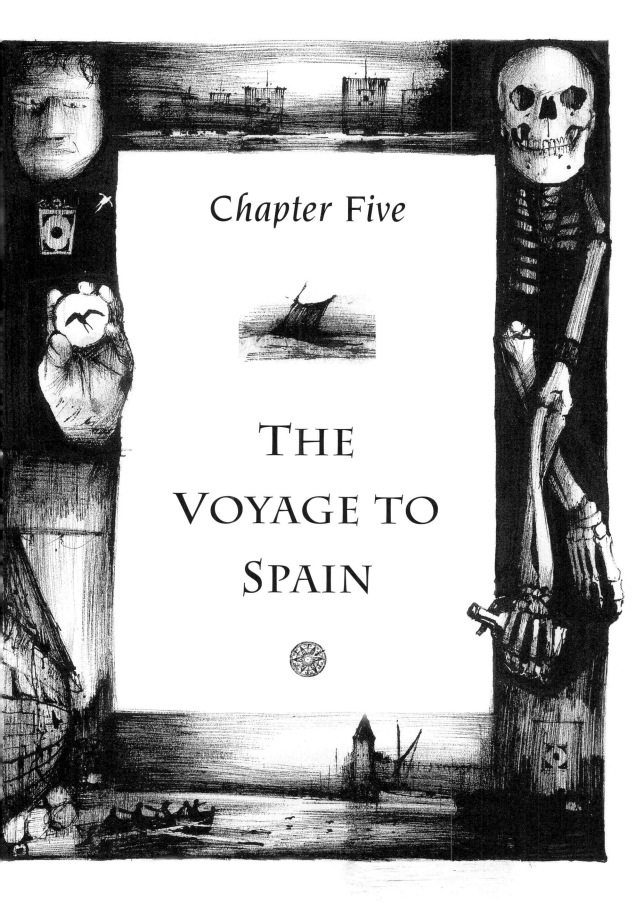

Chapter Five

THE
VOYAGE TO
SPAIN

I
THE VOYAGE BEGINS

IN SUCH A WAY their voyage began.
The Arctic Tern seemed pleased once more
To butt her bows through choppy seas
And rush headlong from England's shore.
The path they took you still can see:
From Sutton Pool they travelled south,
Crossed peaty waters running east
In torrents from the Tamar's mouth.

Under Jennycliffe they sailed,
Around the point to Bovisand
And past the bay where, nights before,
They'd cooked their meal and made their plans.
Then out avoiding Renne's Rocks
(White water marked this the sunken reef –
The Shagstone rising from its tip
Where many ships have come to grief).

A final sighting from the stars
And Bruno swung the helm around.
He set a course for Spanish sun,
And left the curve of Plymouth Sound.
The boat rose on each heaving breaker,
Reached a crest, began to slide
Then launched itself towards the trough
And hurtled headlong down the side.

The heavy seas meant all the crew
Were working hard to tame the sails
And many were the times that waves
Would nearly wash them o'er the rails.
They'd never, though, once even thought
Of running from the howling storm
For Bruno, seeming undisturbed,
Exuded confidence and calm.

And sure enough, the winds died down:
The waves less high, their raging done.
Ahead, a sparkling orange path
Led onwards to a setting sun.
The breeze tugged gently at the lines,
As Adrian prepared a meal.
They ate it seated at their posts,
With Bruno standing at the wheel.

That night, beneath a yellow moon,
They each told tales of voyages past
Of tidal waves, of wrecks and pirates,
Toil and sweat beneath the mast.
And so was passed the time on deck
Till finally, a silence fell
As each man turned expectantly
For Bruno to begin *his* tale . . .

II
BRUNO'S TALE

ONCE UPON A TIME, he said,
At least a thousand years ago
Far to the North, there was a land
Of frozen rivers, ice and snow
Where, in the winter, bitter winds
Could even freeze the waves to glass
Whilst icebergs further out to sea
Would crush the boats which tried to pass.

As spring approached, the ice would melt
And soon bright flowers would surface, where
Not long before, the ground lay hard:
Sweet scent would saturate the air.
The summer days were long and warm
And constant sunlight filled the skies
– Quite different from the winter, when
For months the sun would never rise.

And in those winter months, sometimes
Bright tongues of colour lit the night –
Kaleidoscopes of swirling flames
Called then, as now, the "Northern Lights".
The rivers teemed with countless fish,
Wild geese and deer were often seen:
A place as close to paradise
As could exist outside one's dreams.

The population lived in huts,
And barns were built in which to smoke
The fish their men would catch at sea
And carry home to feed their folk.
These people were content to live
A simple life, would only seek
A shelter from the winter snows
And well-kept stores of fish to eat.

Now in a land not far from this
There lived a very different race.
They hunted, not for food to eat,
But merely to enjoy the chase.
Their life was one of ceaseless war:
They'd plunder all those parts around
Attacking with no cause at all,
Destroying anything they found.

Their leader was a hairy man
Who didn't speak so much as growl.
When happy, he would raise his head,
Stick out his lower jaw, and howl.
His upper jaw held two sharp teeth
A jet black wolf skin was his dress.
His nickname, from his enemies,
Was "Mad Dog" (if you hadn't guessed).

This tyrant wanted to destroy
The lovely land which I've described,
To crush the quiet villages,
Drive out the peaceful fishing tribes.
But just for fun, he thought he'd try
To bring the people to their knees
Without a fight. Could it be done?
He smiled. A plan had been conceived.

He'd send a ship to cruise the coast
And use some trickery, whereby
They'd board a local fishing boat
Whenever one was passing by
And once aboard, they'd offer jewels
To tempt the fisherman to sell
The very land in which he lived –
And all the villagers as well.

He chose the nastiest of men
And told them what they had to do.
They'd take a ship, then wait until
A fishing boat came into view.
They'd start a fire, then shout and scream,
And secretly they'd draw their swords:
The fisherman would come to help
And when he did, they'd leap aboard.

And so it was they stormed a boat,
And pinned the captain to the deck:
Sweat soaked his beard and ran in rivers,
Stained the steel against his neck.
He said that he'd do anything
If only he'd be spared the blade.
Perhaps, they said, they'd let him go . . .
And in return suggest a trade?

He surely couldn't be content
To live a life as poor as this?
A man should not be satisfied
When all he ever owned was fish!
A *real* man wouldn't be content –
Would happily sell all those fools
With whom he lived for something more . . .
. . . Perhaps a bag of precious jewels?

69

With that, a bag of gems was brought
And tipped into his sweaty hand.
He gasped. The wealth now in his palm
Exceeded that in all his land!
With rasping breath and bulging eyes
And pounding heart, he knew that he
Would sell his soul to own these jewels
And pay the price with treachery.

He asked them, then, what they proposed.
What did they want? Quite what, he asked,
Would earn him all these gems he'd seen?
There must be some specific task?
There was, they said. A simple thing –
An evening's work was all he'd trade
And if he did it stealthily
No-one would guess the deal he'd made.

They said they knew that fish was caught
In summer (when the days were fine)
Then smoked and stored in one large hut
To last them through the wintertime.
Without those stores, then all would starve
(The sea which froze up to the shore
Would stop the village fishermen
From putting out to catch some more.)

Within a month, the villagers
Would have no choice but to agree
To any deal which might bring food –
To yield to any enemy.
They'd readily lay down their arms
And surely would make no defence
If those who came brought not just spears,
But food for their deliverance.

It all seemed clear. His life was harsh.
He wanted more, and certainly
Had wondered how he might escape
This life of cold and poverty.
And now this lucky break appeared,
At once appealing to his greed.
He didn't need a second thought.
He seized the chance. At once agreed.

One winter's night when all was ice
He woke and slipped out from his bed
And, making sure he made no noise
Went to the store, just as they'd said.
He stacked the hut with wood he'd saved
Especially for this very night
Then, rubbing two dry sticks together
Set the stack of fuel alight.

He'd made his way back long before
The blazing store was ever found –
Ran with the rest and watched the flames
As burning timbers hit the ground.
He did his best to look distraught
To make them think his feelings true
And to this end (he felt quite pleased)
He even shed a tear or two.

The villagers weren't stupid folk
And every one amongst them knew
The awful peril that they faced,
And just how little they could do.
They all felt sure that they would starve
But worked their hardest nonetheless
To find a way to save themselves,
Whilst meanwhile hoping for the best.

The traitor wasn't too concerned:
He knew that in a week or two
The enemy would all arrive
With not just arms, but foodstuff too.
As time went by, though, doubts appeared.
What could have made them come so late?
It couldn't, surely, be that they
Would leave him, starving, to his fate?

In three months, they'd still not arrived.
The traitor now could clearly see
They'd never planned to come at all:
Saw through their foul duplicity.
By eating scraps he'd tucked away
He barely managed to survive.
When spring arrived, he sat alone
For all the others there . . . had died.

The sea thawed out, and spring had come
Before some ships came into view.
The starving traitor went to meet
The longboats as they landed crew.
He begged for food in pleading tones
And fell before them on his knees.
The Mad Dog threw him gems, and said
"You've earned them – go ahead! Eat these!"

Then Mad Dog raised his head and laughed
Then turned and left the broken man
To watch his tears of deep despair
Cascade like raindrops on the sand.
What good were diamonds? Rubies? Pearls?
These riches couldn't compensate
For what he'd done to all his friends
Repaying love with greed and hate.

He ate some fish caught from the streams
Regained his fitness day by day,
Until at last he had the strength
To load his boat and sail away.
Behind, he left the fishing fleet
Belonging to his friends, now gone.
Condemned to live a nomad life:
To wander through the seas alone.

He'd travelled south for many months
When suddenly a storm arose:
The highest seas and strongest winds
To which he'd ever been exposed.
Through driving rain he turned to shore
And crashed through waves to make his way
Around the foam on Renne's rocks –
Sought shelter then in Cawsand bay.

Next day, he went ashore to rest.
Some houses stood where now you'll find
The Plymouth pub you know so well
(It's called "The Admiral McBride").
The Plymouth people welcomed him,
And fed him bread they'd freshly baked
With local fish and local game
Washed down with frothy ale they made.

He settled to a quiet life –
He fished alone beneath the mast
Still plagued by guilt for all the sins
Committed in his recent past.
At night, he scarcely slept a wink
In troubled dreams, he'd see his friends
Who'd speak to him accusingly,
Demanding that he make amends.

One day, he found he couldn't bear
The awful burden any more.
He moored his boat off Wembury beach
And hurled his gems across the shore.
Then with a rock about his neck
He waded out into the sea.
"These gems, this rock, this sandy beach
Are surely worth far more than me."

He walked out till the icy waves
Which rolled their way from Plymouth Sound
Were splashing up around his face.
He'd take one breath, and soon be drowned.
Then all around the water boiled,
And eerie fog quite suddenly
Appeared – or so it seemed to him –
To well up from the very sea.

And through this fog appeared twelve ships:
Each travelled in the wake before
And made their way towards the man
And dropped their anchors near the shore.
And on each boat, a fisherman
Stepped up and stood along the side
And stared at him from ghostly decks
Which rolled and creaked upon the tide.

He looked in terror through the fog
And instantly he knew the boats.
Nor did it take a second glance
To recognise the fishing folk.
These were his friends whom he had left:
The ones who'd suffered at his hand
Who lay, a thousand miles away,
In icy graves of frozen land.

He all at once confessed his guilt
And told them how a bag of stones
Was traded for the land of theirs –
And even for their very bones.
He said his life was worthless now:
And that he'd thrown away his wealth.
And now, unless they killed him first,
He told them that he'd kill himself.

A ghostly figure made reply.
His punishment would be far worse
Than any death he could devise.
Eternal life would be his curse.
He'd know an awful loneliness,
He'd sit with ages rolling by.
How futile making friends would be
Who in a blink grew old and died.

He'd lift this curse in just one way:
By proving his remorse was true
And if he was to make this clear
There were four things that he must do:
To pay back death – he'd help the sick,
Not take – but give great wealth away,
Not sell – but help the local folk
. . . And save the life of one betrayed.

With this, they went just as they came.
The fog, evaporating, left
A clear blue sky, a flat calm sea,
And not a ripple to suggest
Those ghostly things of which you've heard,
That here a dozen ships passed by
Nor that, in summer, fog had come
To hide the sun in darkened sky.

Still echoing inside his head
He heard the "shopping list" of tasks.
If he should have eternal peace
He must do everything they'd asked.
Some parts were easy – he'd long planned
To help those locals in distress.
But other parts were difficult.
How would he deal with all the rest?

Where could he find a life to save,
Especially of a man betrayed?
And how to come upon huge wealth
Which he could win, then give away?
How could he meet all these demands?
How was he ever to ensure
That he could help the local folk
And tend their sick for ever more?

And with this question, Bruno paused
Then told them that his tale was done.
Lord Hunter wasn't satisfied.
"But was his challenge ever won?
You cannot leave a yarn like that,
A story full of death and greed,
Without a happy ending. Tell us:
Did the fisherman succeed?"

Old Bruno fixed him with his gaze,
Rebuked him gently as he said:
"My story's true and will not end
Until that northern man is dead.
You might not recognise this man
To whom my lengthy tale attests.
So aid each sailor you should meet.
You might just help one find his rest . . ."

III
REACHING SPAIN

THE NEXT FEW DAYS were pleasant ones.
The sea was calm, the air was warm –
In fact, they rapidly forgot
The violence of the early storm.
For meals, they'd cook the scores of fish
Which Hunter caught fresh every day,
While Daisy watched them from the bow,
Her wind-blown fur stiff with salt spray.

The crew enjoyed this brief respite,
But all too soon, a shout was heard.
Their destination wasn't far
For Doctor Chris had seen land-birds.
And sure enough, within the hour
The cliffs of southern Spain were seen.
Lord Hunter strangely knew each part –
He'd seen this coastline in his dream.

They slipped into the port that night.
The sails were furled, then neatly stowed
(Mad Morgan, on the battlements,
Not noticing the ship below).
Before they slept, the crew all talked
Of what the next few days would hold.
But never could they have foreseen
The days of poison, wine . . . and gold . . .

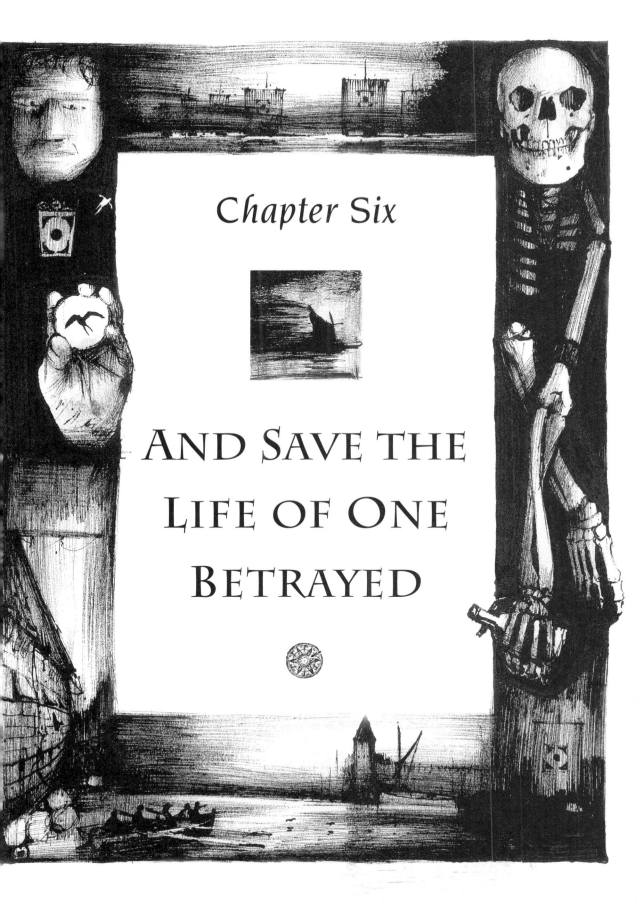

Chapter Six

And Save the
Life of One
Betrayed

I
ASHORE IN SPAIN

THE SPANISH SUN rose warm next morning,
Soaked the sky in dawn's soft light
Which bathed *The Arctic Tern* in gold,
Her burnished timbers glowing bright.
Birds chirruped in the palms around
As traders came to set their stalls:
Fresh fish, or herbs, or vegetables
All sold beneath the castle walls.

Now the warming rays of morning
Soaked the boat and seeped within:
Warmed them gently from their slumbers,
Aided by the shoreline din.
Though they'd settled down exhausted,
Tired from toil beneath the mast,
Now, they woke with some excitement
For, today, they'd start their task.

From the deck there drifted down
The heavy smell of fresh-baked yeast.
Shopping from the stalls already,
Bruno had prepared a feast!
Dripping butter, jugs of juices,
Jams and fruits he'd all prepared.
Wave-made splintered sunrays showered them
As they ate their breakfast there.

Bruno had been hard at work,
And how his night-time toil now showed!
He'd hoisted Daisy overboard
And scrubbed her fur until it glowed.
He'd combed it straight, and now it looked
So clean that Hunter even joked
That given just a minute more
They'd see reflections in her coat!

The dog was not the only one
To whom he'd tended by the dawn.
This, they scarcely could believe:
The captain's head itself was shorn!
He'd combed out knots, and trimmed his beard
And plastered down each errant hair.
Of all the captains in Seville,
He surely was the smartest there!

He'd also donned a naval coat
With gleaming buttons and gold braid.
An anchor badge upon the front,
A brand new cap was on his head.
The Spanish king and noblemen
Would surely have to be impressed
By any seaman of such rank –
Especially one so finely dressed!

The others took the lead he'd set,
All anxious not to fail their Queen.
They'd be the noblest group of men
The Spanish court had ever seen!
Before they left, they gathered up
The things they'd brought from overseas:
Lord Hunter's scroll, and Chris's things –
The precious brooch and Bonsai Tree.

So, thus attired, they made their way
Up through the narrow streets that led
Beside the waterside and on
Towards the castle up ahead.
But as they left the docks behind
They couldn't help but be aware
That something didn't feel quite right.
A heavy sadness filled the air.

Upon the battlements, they saw
The flags all flying at half-mast.
The castle guards were dressed in black
And took no notice as they passed.
"It seems," said Hunter, "all's not well
And, judging from the outward signs
I'd guess that someone here is ill:
It might be that, in fact, they've died."

Arriving at the castle gates,
They told the sentries why they'd come,
Explaining that they couldn't leave
Until their duties had been done.
The English Queen herself, they said,
Had sent a message for the King.
They'd promised that no other man
Should see the scroll – no man but him.

The guards conferred, then let them in
And searched them (just in case they meant
To do some harm, and sabotage
Was actually their true intent.)
The guards addressed them each in turn,
"What's the job you do?" they asked.
The captain, cook and lord replied,
With Doctor Chris explaining last.

At this, the guards all spoke at once,
Excited by the news that here,
Besides a seaman, cook and lord
An Oxford doctor had appeared!
At once they told of how their king
Was dying: that their doctor knew
No more of what the diagnosis was
Than what, to cure him, he might do.

Would Doctor Chris be good enough
To see their king that very day?
For time was short, and all of them
Were sure he'd shortly pass away.
"Of course," said Chris, "I'll help your king.
To aid the sick where'er they're found,
To tend the ill and ease their pain
By oath and honour I am bound."

With that, they hurried to a door
Which opened on some steps of stone
And climbed towards the battlements
To reach the room where lay the throne.
'Twas in this room the king was nursed
Upon a bed he'd had brought there.
The windows overlooked the port.
The room was filled with warm sea air.

They climbed the stairs and reached the top
To find the king collapsed in bed.
So shallow were his gasping breaths
They thought at first that he was dead.
Chris hastened to the dying man
Whose body was so very thin
That bones stuck out at every point
Through wasted flesh and frosted skin.

II
DOCTOR CHRIS
AND THE KING

QUICKLY, CHRIS CALLED all his friends,
And beckoned to the guards around.
"No time to lose! The king will die
Unless a treatment can be found!"
With that, he wrote a list of herbs
With which he planned to make a cure,
And gave it to the guards and crew,
And sent them rushing to the door.

Calling to the household staff
He told them they must fetch a reed,
A gourd, and some fresh water too
Along with salts that he would need.
They did exactly as he said:
Accepted orders readily
For they could see he knew his job
And knowledge gives authority.

Within an hour, they'd all returned.
He took and weighed out every herb
And put them in a mortar bowl
And ground them up without a word.
The household one by one arrived
To watch the doctor as he'd try
To save the king they loved so much,
Who otherwise would surely die.

He took the water, herbs and salts
And quickly mixed them in a flask
Then took his knife and chose a reed
(One which they'd brought just as he'd asked).
The reed was sharpened to a point
And then (which some there thought insane)
He seized the forearm of the king
And slipped the reed into a vein.

A practice common in that day
Meant letting all sick patients bleed.
But not Chris Edge, who planned to give
His herbal liquid through the reed.
He thus knelt down beside the bed
And through the reed dripped medicine
Until at last the final drops
Had reached the royal blood within.

An hour went by. The household watched.
Then some of them began to cry
For this must be a miracle!
The king improved before their eyes!
Still clearly sick, his skin was moist,
His eyes no longer deep and glazed.
Within an hour, this doctor's work
Had made him better than for days!

III
A REUNION FOR HUNTER

JUST AT THAT MOMENT, heads all turned
As someone swept in through the door
(A nobleman, they might have guessed,
To judge by all the silks he wore).
Just in time, he saw the crowd
And slipped a crown from off his head
(Indecent haste would not seem good:
He'd wait until the king was dead).

It seemed they knew him, liked him too
For servants all around them bowed:
But Daisy, at Lord Hunter's feet,
Just bared her teeth, and snarled and growled.
A guard, saluting him, announced:
"Lord Morgan, merchant, and our heir."
Lord Hunter, though, knew him at once . . .
He knew the pirate standing there!

For Hunter well remembered him,
That face burned in his memory –
The "Mad Dog" who had sunk his ship,
And tried to bury him at sea.
Good fortune, though, was his that day
For though they stood there eye to eye,
The Mad Dog didn't recognise
The captain (who he thought had died).

Lord Hunter found himself bemused.
What could have brought the Mad Dog here?
How had a common thug become
A powerful Spanish courtier?
And worse, if now the king had died
(As well he might with Chris not there)
It seemed from what the guard had said
That Mad Dog Morgan was his heir!

Whatever else it might have been,
It wasn't chance he held such sway.
What had Morgan done to get here,
Standing where his sick king lay?
He'd have to speak with Doctor Chris
At any opportunity.
What had made the king so ill?
And were there signs of treachery?

Morgan was himself confused.
That morning, just a glance could tell:
The king would surely die by noon.
Oh, yes! The plan was going well!
He felt like shouting out for joy
But somehow now he masked his glee
And wrung his hands, and sobbed and shook
In (quite convincing) misery.

He'd thought he'd have a drink, maybe,
And wait until the morning passed,
And then (he hoped) return to find
His "Noble King" had breathed his last.
His years of scheming would pay off.
The castle, colonies, and power,
Great wealth, the throne, this crown he held,
Would all be his within the hour!

Returning, something seemed amiss.
The crowd, it's true, was round the bed
Just as he'd pictured they would be
If summoned when the king was dead.
But no-one seemed to be distressed.
In fact, on coming through the door
He'd sensed a joy and . . . goodness me!
The king looked *better* than before!

His jaw dropped and his eyes popped out.
He couldn't catch his breath. He swayed.
This couldn't be! What had become
Of all the plans that he had made?
And then he noticed strangers there.
What did they want? Who could they be?
(And why, with one, was he aware
Of strange familiarity?)

The guards mistook his shock for joy
(So gripped was he with frank alarm).
They ran to help the swaying lord
And led him gently by the arm.
They sat him down, and said they'd known
Their prayers were answered, and that fate
Was on their side when they first saw
Four Englishmen approach the gate.

Now Morgan heard how Doctor Chris
Had worked a miracle indeed
With herbs and water, salts and such
Delivered through a hollow reed.
At this he had to force a smile
Despite the fact that, deep inside,
He felt no happiness at all
To find his ruler still alive.

He had to act. But what to do?
He'd rather die than e'er allow
The scheme on which he'd worked so long
To come so far then falter now.
He couldn't just dismiss these men
(Such action would invite dissent).
Oh, no. He'd have to welcome them
Then make their absence "permanent".

He therefore stood and praised Chris Edge
And all the friends with whom he came,
And welcomed them with open arms
And thanked them on behalf of Spain.
He asked them if they'd honour him
By not returning to the sea:
Instead remain, accept from him
Some Spanish hospitality?

By nightfall, then, they'd settled in.
Grand staterooms had been found for all,
And even Daisy had a place
On cushions laid out in the hall.
But Doctor Chris declined a room
And asked that rugs be brought instead
And laid out on the marble floor:
He'd sleep beside his patient's bed.

By morning, Chris was feeling tired
Through tending to his patient's health.
The king improved and slept quite well –
Chris hardly got a wink himself!
But nonetheless, he felt relieved
To find that, by the morning light,
The king looked so much better now
Than when the sun went down last night.

At eight o'clock Lord Morgan came
And humbly said he'd do his share
In caring for his stricken king
And play his part in nursing care.
Chris left, but glanced back from the door
As Morgan started pouring sips
Of some sweet Spanish wine he'd brought,
Between the sleeping monarch's lips . . .

IV
A PLAN CONCEIVED

THE DOCTOR WENT to find his friends.
He didn't want to make a fuss,
But medically he'd noticed things
Which urgently they should discuss.
He found them in the banquet hall.
A meal quite fit for heads of state
Was laid out there – great mounds of fruit
And sweetmeats piled upon each plate.

Chris joined them for a hearty meal,
But secretly he slipped a note
Across the table to his friends:
"There's danger! Meet me on the boat!"
They nodded, and said nothing then,
But after breakfast made their way
Beyond the castle walls, and down
To where their wooden vessel lay.

Once there, Lord Hunter took the chair
And said he also had concerns
But first they'd hear the doctor speak
Who'd tell them all of what he'd learned.
Chris stood, and paced the cabin deck.
"I don't know who would do this thing
But clear as day, a traitor's hand
Is poisoning the Spanish king!"

"The symptoms and the signs are clear:
No other thing has made him sick.
His food or drink is laced for sure
With deadly poisonous arsenic!
We have to flush the traitor out,
And each of us must try to find
A way to halt the king's supply,
For he'll recover, given time."

A quiet smile crossed Bruno's lips.
Perhaps this was a chance to save
A very special sort of life –
"The life of one who'd been betrayed."
Lord Hunter stood then with a grin,
Announced that they might be surprised
To learn that he already knew
The man who threatened royal lives!

Of course, the others all had heard
Of how Lord Hunter once escaped
A death at sea in pirate hands
(How Bruno saved him from that fate.)
"I'd not forget that pirate's face,
Would know him if we met again.
Lord Morgan and that evil man
I tell you, are one and the same!"

"Although I know the traitor's name,
He'll always say in his defence
That claims like these are quite absurd.
If true, where is the evidence?
We have to somehow prove his guilt
But stop him doing any harm,
But nothing that we say or do
Should cause him even slight alarm."

They sat together for a while,
As each tried hard to make a plan
To stop Mad Morgan's evil scheme
And meanwhile not alert the man.
The cook piped up. Had he heard right?
And was he really right to think
That poison only reached the king
Mixed in his food or in his drink?

If that were true, it seemed to him
That drink must be the likely way:
The most the king could do was sip –
He can't have eaten now for days.
"I'll volunteer to be a cook
And in the kitchen check what's passed
Through every bottle, vat or bowl
To end up in his drinking glass."

"Meanwhile, I think that one of us
Should always stay and watch the king.
Between us, we can keep him safe
From any further poisoning.
And finally, I also think
That Daisy should remain there too.
I know no better guard than she:
She's loyal, tireless, brave and true."

The logic was impeccable.
They all agreed with Adrian
That these suggestions, put together,
Made a truly first-rate plan!
So one by one they left the boat
All keen at once to make a start,
While Daisy, trotting on behind,
Seemed happy that she'd play her part.

V
DISCOVERY

BACK AT THE CASTLE, the plan was beginning.
They sat down with Morgan to eat at midday
Then Hunter arose, banged the table for silence
And said to them all that he'd something to say.
He felt much aggrieved that a lowly ship's cook
Should be treated the same as a lord such as he.
More fitting that Adrian served in the kitchen:
Lord Morgan, he hoped, would be pleased to agree?

Now Morgan thought this was a splendid idea,
To embarrass a servant in front of them all
So he quickly agreed, and at once called the guards
To drag Adrian out from the banqueting hall.
"I'm sorry," he said, "for the fact that this man
Should embarrass you all by the way he's behaved.
You can now be assured that he'll just do his job:
No longer 'a lord', he's now back as a slave."

And so it was easy to start on the plan,
And with Adrian now well installed as the cook
He was able to keep a close eye on the servants
And check all the drinks that the sickly king took.
Meanwhile, Doctor Chris had announced his intention
To sleep by the king, and ensure someone stayed
In the room at all times to administer medicines
And tend him, and bathe him, and act as nursemaid.

The pile of silk cushions were moved from the hallway
And laid on the throne, on which Daisy would sleep.
Being banned, back at home, from the beds, chairs or carpets,
To sleep on a *throne* was a staggering treat!
All the while Mad Dog seethed, for this irksome intrusion
Could easily leave him with all his plans wrecked.
But he couldn't complain lest his motives were questioned
When one of the household might come to suspect.

In the following days, Doctor Chris kept a watch
And was cunning in all that he did for the king.
He would take all the food and the drink that was brought
But would secretly throw it away in the bin.
Captain Bruno, in turn, would come visiting often
With fresh fruit and vegetables hidden each time
Which he'd pass to the doctor when no-one was looking
Along with a bottle of replacement wine.

With careful attention, and all Chris's medicines,
The signs of improvement were steady and sure.
Although much relieved, this made Chris very anxious
For he didn't want Morgan to know of the cure.
As soon as the king was of sound enough mind,
Doctor Chris spoke in detail of all that had passed.
He said that the king should pretend to be dying
Should anyone enter, or questions be asked.

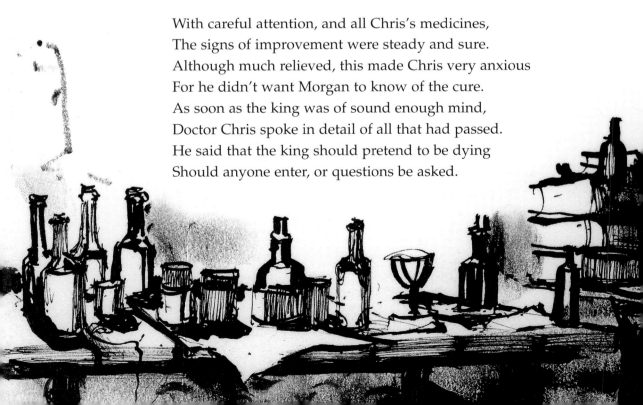

The king was astonished, and shocked by the news.
He couldn't believe that Lord Morgan was blamed –
That this man who had nursed him throughout recent weeks
And a murdering cur could be one and the same.
Nonetheless, he agreed that he'd follow advice
And would do everything that the doctor had asked –
For if innocent, then Morgan's name would be cleared
But if guilty, the king could then take him to task.

Meanwhile, in the kitchen, young Adrian worked
For the plan gave each one of them tasks they must do.
So he slaved at his cooking, but watched from the shadows,
Made efforts to find how the poison got through.
He noted quite quickly that fresh food was purchased
From different people or markets each day
And that no-one complained if he cooked it himself
Or delivered it up to the king on a tray.

He thought it unlikely that food was the source,
And by logic was steadily forced to suspect
That the wine must be poisoned, but strangely he saw
That the servants could drink it without ill effect.
He nearly gave up in despair more than once
For he just couldn't see how the traitor arranged
For the poison to get to the king. Then one night
He observed something happen which seemed very strange . . .

In the hope that he might catch the culprit red-handed,
He'd taken to hiding himself out of sight
By the side of a stove (which could be very hot!)
Where he'd rest, huddled up, through uncomfortable nights.
At about two o'clock, while the household all slept,
He awoke to the sound of a creak from the door
And the sound of soft footsteps, as someone came quietly
And furtively tiptoed across the stone floor.

Now Adrian froze, and at once held his breath
While the visitor paused as he listened for sound.
The visitor snooped round the kitchen and pantry
In case there was anyone else still around.
At last he seemed satisfied no-one was watching:
He walked to another door, undid the locks;
Slipping out down some steps to return minutes later,
Then walked to the table and laid down a box.

Not five minutes later, more footsteps were heard
And the first man turned round as a second walked in.
Though the face of Lord Morgan was hidden in shadows,
Still Adrian knew straight away it was him.
The first man was also well known in the castle –
And Adrian, even at night, knew him too:
He worked in the kitchen as "cook to the king" –
'Twas the one Morgan called from his pirate ship's crew.

From the box, he withdrew two full bottles of wine
Which were marked on the label with small yellow dots.
In return, Morgan passed him a pair which were empty,
And these the cook took and then hid in the box.
The cook told Lord Morgan he'd added the poison
And each of the bottles now held three grains more.
Just a glass now would kill, and to mask the strong taste
He had made the wine sweeter than ever before.

Lord Morgan spoke briefly. He'd planned that the king
Should have regular doses of poison in wine.
In this way, his illness would come on quite slowly,
And no-one would think Morgan caused his decline.
But now, with these Englishmen nursing the king
It proved hard to deliver a steady supply
Of the poisonous wine to the lips of the king –
And he'd mixed a strong dose to be sure that he died.

He'd take up a bottle of wine to the throne room
And pour both the doctor and monarch a drink.
They'd have just a glass, but would then swiftly die –
Of contagious disease (or so people would think.)
After all, they all knew that their king had been ill
And the doctor had sat a long time by his side.
They'd assume that some plague had afflicted the king
And from this both the doctor and he now had died.

Now Morgan, his treachery done, left the room.
The cook took his leave and slipped from the side door
Taking with him the box (which now held the old bottles),
Returned (empty handed) as fast as before.
A few moments later, the cook and Lord Morgan
Had slipped from the room with their treachery done.
Alone, in the corner, poor Adrian sat –
Not daring to breathe until sure they'd both gone.

At breakfast next morning, he went from the kitchen
And served at the table where all his friends sat.
While pouring their tankards of juice, he made sure
To tip half of the jug into Lord Hunter's lap!
Lord Hunter leapt up, and at once cursed the servant.
He'd never before met a clumsier man!
He bowed to Lord Morgan, and strode from the table
Then marched to the washroom beside Adrian.

On the way to the washroom, Lord Hunter yelled loudly
But all the while listened as Adrian talked.
Succinctly, he told of the meeting he'd witnessed
And finished recounting his tale as they walked.
When Morgan arrived at the washrooms on tiptoe
To listen outside to the things they discussed
All he heard was the cook as he begged for forgiveness
And Hunter himself as he stood there and cursed.

Lord Hunter made sure that his movements weren't seen,
Telling Chris and the Spanish king all that he knew:
How Adrian listened to Mad Morgan's meeting
And now was aware of what Morgan would do.
The king now believed that Lord Morgan was guilty,
For how else could Hunter have known of the times
When this merchant had tended him throughout his illness
And plied him with glasses of sweet-tasting wine?

There still was no proof that Lord Morgan was guilty:
The king said, without it, he wouldn't react.
He'd wait in his bed until poison was brought:
In this way would Morgan be caught in the act.
The doctor tried hard to explain that this course
Was a dangerous one, for if Morgan were trapped
He'd have nothing to lose and might try something rash –
He might even resort to a violent attack.

But the king had decided. They'd just have to wait.
He would do what was right. Leave the outcome to fate . . .

VI
THE TRAITOR CAUGHT

THE NEXT DAYS were tense as they waited for Morgan
To make his last efforts to usurp the crown.
The stakes now were high, and they knew of the risks
Which the king, by his actions, had chosen to run.
Lord Hunter was put in a difficult spot,
For he wished at all times to keep guard on the throne.
But if Morgan should see him or Bruno around
He might notice the trap, and might therefore back down.

The hours turned to days, and Lord Morgan did nothing,
Behaved to them all as a perfect host would.
He met them at meal times, and asked of their health,
And made sure every comfort was theirs if he could.
They all thought that, maybe, he'd somehow got warning,
His strike now subjected to untold delay.
That night, though, as all were retiring to bed
Lord Morgan walked in with some wine on a tray.

In the room, Doctor Chris was alone with the king
When Lord Morgan arrived and then bowed to the bed.
The king could see clearly the small yellow dot
Which was marked on the label, as Adrian said.
Lord Morgan announced that he'd come with a nightcap:
– No better a tonic, he said, at such times
Than an evening of friendship and good sleep to follow,
All aided by glasses of sweet Spanish wine.

The king smiled and nodded. He sat up, and said
That he felt so much better now Morgan was here.
A true friend indeed, he had only to come
And the throne room was filled all at once with good cheer.
He'd therefore be pleased if Lord Morgan would join them:
How rude it would be if the king slaked his thirst!
Instead he would pour a fresh glass from the bottle
And Morgan would honour him, drinking it first.

He handed a glass to Lord Morgan and nodded.
"My friend," said the king, "let us drink to your health!"
Lord Morgan's hand shook. All his plans lay in ruins.
He'd failed in his bid for the crown and its wealth.
The king's smile was frozen, and so was the doctor's.
They clearly had heard of his treacherous game.
He shattered the glass on the bedstead beside him!
The king and the doctor would die just the same!

He pulled out a dagger from under his cloak
Then he rushed at the king with it over his head.
He couldn't care less if they knew it was murder:
His only concern was the king should be dead!
For a moment, it seemed that he might have succeeded
(For the king, moving slowly, was sure to be harmed)
When Daisy howled loudly and dived from the throne
To sink all her teeth, from mid-air, in his arm.

He screamed as the dagger was dropped from his grasp.
Daisy hung there and snarled (while still wagging her tail:
After all, she'd been given silk cushions and thrones,
And, completing her pleasure, a good fight as well!)
The more Morgan struggled and hit the poor dog,
The more she determined she'd put up a show.
She'd stay there till Christmas if given the chance
And if Chris didn't stop her, might never let go!

But Chris acted quickly and ran to the bell-pull,
And rang it to summon the guards to arrive.
He rushed at Lord Morgan and hurled himself forwards –
Crashed into his legs with an elegant dive.
They fell to the floor and were struggling there
With the dagger still lying not far out of reach
(Though Morgan had no luck in trying to reach it
With Daisy still clamped to his arm like a leech!)

Bruno and Adrian followed the soldiers
With Hunter (they'd noticed the guards rushing past.)
The king gave the orders, and Morgan was shackled
And led from the room with his arms firmly grasped.
The king, though quite shaken, stood up by his bed
And then thanked all his friends who had saved him that night.
Picking up Morgan's dagger, he asked them to kneel
And then dubbing their shoulders, made each of them knights.

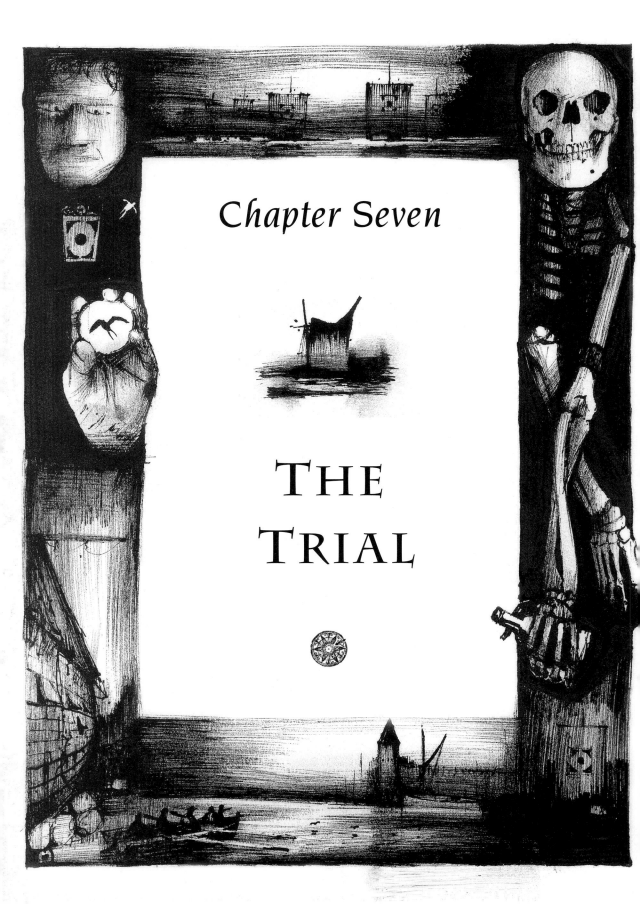

Chapter Seven

THE TRIAL

I
RELAXATION

THE MONTHS THAT CAME were paradise.
The warm waves lapped the sun-soaked shore
And scented winds seeped through each door.
The nights were filled with food and rest
And all agreed, these were the best
Of days that they would ever share
And happily they rested there.
The king grew ever stronger now
And walked each day (if Chris allowed)
Along the seafront, past the stalls
Where joyful greetings came from all.

The crew were feted by the crowds
Who sought to drape their necks in flowers
And pressed upon them gifts each day,
And with each present, they would say
How much they owed these Englishmen
Who'd done such good for all of them.
And even Daisy found herself
Recipient of untold wealth –
More bones than any dog had seen
Outside the best of canine dreams!

The Arctic Tern, beside the shore,
Was somehow different from before:
The fittings, once of tarnished brass
Now glinted as of gold and glass.
Her paintwork shone as if brand new,
Her mast looked newly polished, too.
Quite how such changes came to be
Remained a total mystery:
The crew were baffled to a man,
Though Bruno seemed to understand.
He'd sometimes smile as he'd inspect
The glowing timbers of the deck.

Beneath the castle on the hill
(Which overlooked this town, Seville)
Lay many dungeons – cold dank rooms
Off miles and miles of catacombs,
And townsfolk could be heard to tell
How these were used as prison cells.
In truth, the king would not condone
Or order from his regal throne
The use of these facilities
For any purpose such as this.
No matter what his crime might be,
Each man should keep his dignity.

In comfort, then, above the gate
Lord Morgan sat, consumed with hate.
From windows, he'd hear people sing
The praises of both crew and king
And bitterly he'd curse these curs!
These interfering foreigners!
His evil mind at once was set.
By Jove! He'd not be beaten yet!
He surely yet would find a way
To take revenge another day
And in some future time and place
He'd wipe the smile off every face.

He thus pretended to the guards
That now he'd had a change of heart:
Regretted what he'd done, and would
Redress the balance if he could.
He begged them to stand up in court
And tell the king that they now thought
His punishment should never be
A life in jail. Could they not see?
A better sentence at the trial
Would be a life spent in exile:
He'd then be free to help the poor,
Repent for what had gone before.

A month went by before the king
Was well enough to set a date
On which a jury would be called
To judge the man, decide his fate.
Until that time, Lord Morgan tried
Much harder with each passing day
To make the guards believe he'd changed,
And tried to make them use their sway.

The crew, meanwhile, enjoyed their stay.
As weeks went by they all agreed
That soon the king would be quite well
And then would be the time to leave.
They'd stay, they said, until the trial:
Felt sure that by such time as this
The king would be completely fit,
Not needing help from Doctor Chris.

The king consulted with them all,
Accepting what they had to say
And thanked them for the help he'd had
And that they had agreed to stay.
He asked that they attend the trial
As many there might hold a grudge.
Impartial to the state's affairs,
They'd see Lord Morgan fairly judged.

Excitement mounted in the port.
The citizens were keen to see
How king and jury would behave
And what the sentence was to be.
For since the king had come to power
No criminal had met his fate
By torture, floggings or the rack
Nor execution by the state.

But surely this must be the case
Where noble thoughts would soon give way
To vengeance by the king himself
Who'd make sure Morgan's debt was paid?
The people guessed the king would call
For Morgan to be hung: he'd see
That any man who crossed him thus
Would pay the price of treachery.

The trial date came. The court was packed
With citizens from far and wide.
It seemed that all of Spain had come
To hear the truth – themselves decide
What fate Lord Morgan should have earned.
In fact, they'd all made up their minds:
They'd back their king, who'd call for death
As payment for Lord Morgan's crimes.

The trumpets blew, and flags unfurled.
The gathered throng moved to each side
And knelt upon their bended knees
As king and courtiers arrived.
Behind them came the Englishmen.
They walked in silence to their seats,
Then settled down to hear the trial
With Daisy snoozing at their feet.

A moment later, came the guards
Escorting Morgan wrapped in chains.
For sympathy, he dragged one foot
And shook his head as if in pain.
His gaze directed to the floor,
He feigned a look of misery:
He turned towards the throne and bowed
(How well he faked humility!)

The king then turned to face the crowd.
Lord Morgan was accused, he said
Of making plans to kill the king,
Then wear the crown himself, instead!
The king, as victim of this plot,
Admitted he must bear a grudge.
And couldn't act impartially.
Would Bruno therefore be the judge?

The court now heard the evidence.
And all were shocked at what they heard.
In fact, just like a pantomime,
They gasped or booed at every word!
They learned of Morgan's other life:
Of how he'd lived from piracy,
And how he'd once sunk Hunter's boat
And left him there to drown at sea.

They heard how Morgan loathed the king
And how he'd thus conceived a plan:
He'd wormed his way inside the court
To be the sovereign's right-hand man.
A pirate now replaced the cook
Who smuggled poisoned wine inside
Which Morgan served his trusting king –
And planned to do so till he died.

They heard how fate now intervened
And how *The Arctic Tern* arrived:
How Doctor Chris had found the king
Just hours before he would have died.
Of how he'd saved him – diagnosed
The reason why the king was sick:
How Adrian had found that wine
Had borne the deadly arsenic.

A hush descended on the court:
The climax of the tale described
How Morgan, on discovery,
Had drawn a dagger from by his side.
The crowd drew breath (and others cheered)
When told how Daisy saved the day
By hanging from Lord Morgan's arm.
The court let out a loud 'Hooray!'

Old Bruno said there was no doubt:
That Morgan's guilt was clear as day.
But was there anything at all
The prisoner might wish to say?
For every man should have his chance
To stand and plead his innocence
And face the men accusing him
And speak some words in self defence.

Lord Morgan rose and cleared his throat
(Pretending to be choked with guilt)
And shook with fear and frank remorse
(Emotions which he'd never felt!)
He said he had no good excuse:
His guilt was plain for all to see.
He'd seen the error of his ways,
And pleaded now for clemency.

Old Bruno turned and faced the king.
Beyond all doubt, he said, they'd shown
That Morgan was a guilty man
Who'd had designs upon the throne.
It wasn't down to foreigners
To pass a sentence on the man.
The power to judge lay with the state,
And with its head, the Spanish Crown.

The king stood up, and thanked his friend.
Before he'd say another word
He'd thank these men for all they'd done,
The heroes of the tale they'd heard.
If Englishmen behaved like this
He'd gladly have them all as friends.
From this time forth, they had his pledge:
The feud with Spain was at an end.

And in that spirit, he would show
That peace was better than a war.
A man, if wronged, must set aside
His anger at what went before.
Lord Morgan could walk free that day –
Indeed, he'd take a bag of gold
And live in exile from the land
And help the poor, the sick, the old.

With that, the king called to the guards
To loose the chains that held the man
And take him to his boat nearby,
And see it safely far from land.
And just before he left the room,
He shook Lord Morgan's hand and said
That he forgave him all he'd done.
To others he must pay his debts.

Lord Morgan packed, and in disgrace
Was walked by guards beside the sea.
The townsfolk watched him board his ship
And glared in silence from the quay.
He hoisted sails, sailed from the port
And as he left the Spanish shore
He raised the pirate flag aloft.
He'd take revenge! On that he swore . . .

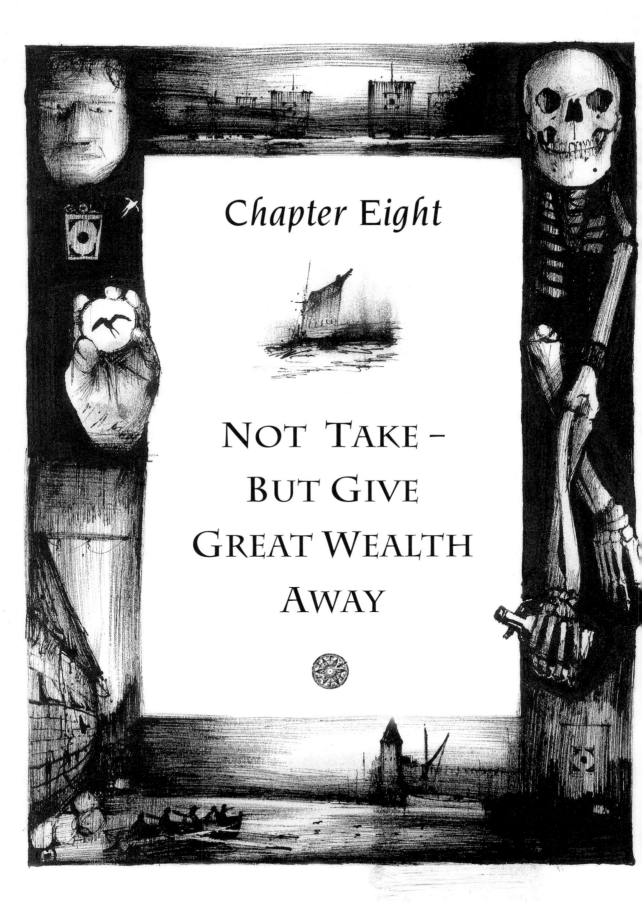

Chapter Eight

Not Take –
But Give
Great Wealth
Away

I
GOING HOME

A WEEK AFTER THIS, and the Englishmen packed.
The time had now come when they had to return.
Their mission was finished. The Queen would be waiting.
Of peace with the Spanish she shortly would learn.
Before they had gone, though, the king called them in
And he privately thanked them for all they had done:
The debt which he owed them could not be repaid
And he cared for them all as if each was a son.

He handed Lord Hunter a scroll of pale parchment
He'd sealed with red wax and a ribbon of gold.
It offered full peace with the English in future,
And in it the tale of their valour was told.
He'd made it quite clear that he might not have trusted
Ambassadors, messengers . . . men of that kind.
But these were unlike any men he had known.
It was through their compassion this treaty was signed.

And now to old Bruno he turned and spoke softly.
He'd seen, in a dream, twelve ships moored in the bay.
And the captain of one had called out to the king.
When he reached him the captain then had this to say,
"You must take out a chest – get the biggest you have –
And then fill it with silver and Pieces of Eight.
You must give it to Bruno to carry away,
He will know what to do: it's his means of escape."

Now Chris thanked the king for his words and the scroll,
Said the pleasure of helping was truly their own.
They'd little to leave as a gift from them all
(To a man with the wealth which belonged to the throne!)
Even so, they would leave him a token of friendship –
His wife, he explained, made a brooch with great pride:
'Twas her finest creation, in silver and gold,
With the heads of his daughters arranged side by side.

The doctor bowed deeply. The king took the present
And wore it with pride from that day to his last,
And such brooches were soon thought the height of good taste:
You can see them in paintings of centuries past.
(They were made in both silver and gold, and enamel,
And porcelain versions were soon to abound:
They had heads set in white, on a background of blue:
In antique shops, museums or stores they're still found.)

Doctor Chris also gave him the gift which he'd carried
For hundreds of miles over wild stormy seas:
The king was delighted, for never before
Had he seen an example of such 'Bonsai trees'.
They went off to pack, while the king filled a chest
With a mountain of coinage and Pieces of Eight:
To carry the chest down to Old Bruno's boat
Needed four on each side, on account of its weight!

II
TREACHERY AGAIN

BY NIGHT-TIME, the chest had been loaded aboard,
And the struggle meant all of the townsfolk now knew
What the chest must contain. And the word of these riches
Reached not just the honest, but evil men too.
And from a dark corner, a trader was watching:
He'd only that day come and set up his stall.
And, strangely for someone who seemed to be selling,
He didn't display any items at all . . .

He carried a constant companion beside him:
A parrot which lived in a large iron cage.
With green and gold feathers, but cold evil eyes
If disturbed, it would hiss or would squawk in a rage.
This ill-tempered bird was called "Dolly" – a name
Which much later, in tales of this time, was misheard.
And so, here in England, you'll find "Polly Parrot"
Is used as a name by the owners of birds.

On the arm of the trader was found a tattoo
'Twas an octopus glaring with fiery red eyes.
If you think back, you've heard of a similar motif
Which flew on a pirate flag raised to the skies,
For this innocent trader was really a pirate –
A spy who'd been sent to be sure Morgan learned
Of such time as the Englishmen seemed to be packing
To leave on their vessel – the ship *Arctic Tern*.

On hearing that treasure was now being loaded,
The pirate decided his master must know.
He opened the cage of his bird (Dolly Parrot)
And whispered to her that she'd soon have to go.
He wrote out a letter in which he explained
That the Englishmen's boat carried treasure aboard:
By nightfall, the crew would have made preparations,
And surely, at dawn, they'd set sail for abroad.

He fastened the note round the leg of the parrot:
Released her to fly back to Lord Morgan's hands
So he'd learn that same day of the news from Seville
And could quickly react and prepare detailed plans.
Now Morgan, till then, had but one aim in life:
He had wanted to ambush and sink Bruno's boat.
But he spotted the chance to do better than that
When that evening the parrot arrived with the note.

His vessel was hidden within a small cove
Not a half-hour away from where Bruno's was moored.
He sailed, then, at midnight – by one had arrived:
He dropped anchor: a longboat was slipped overboard.
Six pirates crouched low by the sides of the boat
And they silently paddled their way 'cross the sea
Past a sleeping Seville and along through the harbour
Then clambered their way up the walls of the quay.

In shadow, the men crept towards Bruno's boat
Where stood guards (that the king had insisted be left)
Who were tired from the work which they'd done through the day
And the effort of loading the full treasure chest.
It was therefore quite easy to sneak down the quay
And from there they were able to launch their attack.
They boarded the ship in a matter of seconds.
The guards they'd knocked out were left trussed up in sacks.

A longboat was moored to *The Arctic Tern*'s bow
And was loaded with treasure heaved over the side.
They strapped it down safely, pushed off from the *Tern*,
Then, rowing in silence, slipped out on the tide.
The Arctic Tern lay in a glassy sea surface:
There wasn't a wave, and no breath of wind stirred.
Yet gently at first, then with increasing fury,
She rolled and she pitched, and her bell was soon heard.

Above, in the castle, Old Bruno was sleeping
But what woke him up he could not really say.
His breath short and quiet, he sat and he listened:
The sound of the bell drifted up from the bay!
The rest of his crew had themselves been awoken
And rushed from their rooms, and descended the stairs,
Grabbing bags as they went, they ran out from the castle
And burst through the gate to the cold morning air.

Seized with fear, Bruno panicked – he knew right away
That the chest had been stolen while he was asleep.
He had given his word that he'd give wealth away,
And this promise was one he intended to keep.
His freedom demanded he cared for the sick,
That he went to the rescue of one man betrayed.
He'd succeeded in that, saved the life of the king:
Till he'd sacrificed wealth, though, his debt wasn't paid.

Sure enough, at the boat, all the guards were trussed up.
When released, they explained that six men had appeared.
They had recognised one as a close friend of Morgan's:
The chest had been stolen, as Bruno had feared.
Bruno asked when it happened – they must be precise –
Just how long had it been since all this had gone on?
They were told that the pirates had only just left:
It was not half an hour since their boat must have gone.

Only twelve hours before had the treasure been loaded,
Yet Morgan had heard, and had stolen the chest.
They'd sneaked in by longboat. These facts all suggested
He must be close by to have managed the theft.
They'd ready their boat, and must put out to sea!
They'd give chase to the pirates – wherever they'd run!
They'd take what was theirs, and defeat Mad Dog Morgan.
They'd do what was right, and see justice was done!

III
THE CHASE

AS ONE, they leapt aboard the ship –
They couldn't waste a moment's time.
With Adrian behind the wheel,
Lord Hunter slashed the mooring lines.
Bruno hauled to hoist the sails,
Sweat on his forehead as he scowled.
While Daisy, standing on the bow
Drew breath, then raised her head . . . and howled.

By now, the pirate thieves were back –
Had hauled their booty to the deck
When suddenly Lord Morgan froze:
The hairs were prickling on his neck.
A ghostly howl had reached his ears
(Though, strangely, not those of his men)
And never had he felt such fear
As that which welled within him then.

The Arctic Tern was after him –
He knew the truth instinctively.
And this time, if they captured him,
He'd not slip free so easily.
He panicked – knew he had to run
And find some lonely hiding place.
He'd sail at once, and head for Crete
And soon lose Bruno in the chase.

With Dolly perched upon his arm
And skull and crossbones flying high,
He raised the anchor, set the sails,
Turned East as dawn lit up the sky.
Pathetic people! Fools to think
They'd catch him quite that easily.
He'd teach them not to mess around
With such a shrewd adversary!

The Arctic Tern by now was off:
A wind had risen suddenly
Which wrenched the sails and sped the boat
Through spume and surf and mounting seas.
But which way should they go from here?
Lord Hunter shouted in despair.
Their quest was lost before the start
For Morgan could be anywhere.

Filled with fear and loneliness
He sank down, beaten, to his knees
When through the darkness, clear as day,
He heard the voice of dear Louise.
"Think of me should you be threatened,
Scared, or when you feel alone:
Call my name: I'll send a guide
To bring you safely back to home."

He shut his eyes, and thought of her
At home in Durham far away.
And as she slept, he called to her:
"I need you now", she heard him say.
"Please guide us where we need to go,
Just as you promised you would do:
So calm my fears, and help me now
And see me safely back to you."

And in her dreams, Louise arose
And gazed at him without a word.
She held her hands above her head
And from them flew a snow-white bird.
Lord Hunter stood, walked to the bow
Then turned his head towards the skies
In time to see the bird appear
And ride the winds before his eyes.

He called to Bruno. "Trust me now,
I cannot tell you how I know,
But following that bird you see
Will take us where we want to go!"
Old Bruno swung the helm around
And chased the rays of dawn's first light
The Arctic Tern was rushing East
As Daisy howled into the night.

Lord Morgan's temper now was frayed.
Despite the waves brought by the squall,
And wind behind them for an hour,
They'd covered not one yard at all.
And through this time he'd heard those howls
From Bruno's dog – and now the din
Grew louder as each minute passed:
They'd followed, and were closing in!

How could they trail his every move?
How had they known which way to head?
They seemed to know where he had moored,
And also, which way he had fled!
But still he'd fool them – turn around
And unlit by the morning sun,
He'd sneak right past them in the dark
And head back West the way he'd come.

Aboard *The Arctic Tern*, the crew
Were sailing with the bird in sight,
When suddenly it banked above
And turned South-West. That wasn't right!
But Hunter told them not to fear –
The pirate boat had doubled back
In efforts to evade the chase
And throw the hunters off the track.

Just as they turned, the wind swung too
And rushed with force from Spanish shores.
It filled the sails, and heeled them over
Driven faster than before.
And now, just as the sun appeared
Old Bruno took his telescope
And, following the bird above,
He caught a glimpse of Morgan's boat.

From high up on the pirate mast
Lord Morgan's lookout yelled: he'd seen
The Arctic Tern not far behind,
And gaining with alarming speed!
Lord Morgan twitched. His face went white.
His body dripped with icy sweat.
Deep down, he knew the game was lost
But still, he'd not give in just yet!

So, all that day Lord Morgan fled.
His ship ran South before the gale
And made the greatest speed she could
By hoisting each and every sail.
His crew threw all they had away
To make the vessel travel light.
Perhaps they might maintain their lead
And lose Old Bruno in the night . . .

Lord Morgan's confidence now grew.
He knew it couldn't be too far
Before they'd cross the narrow straits
And reach the North of Africa.
Here, under cover of the night,
They'd slip through waters he knew well.
Old Bruno, if he dared pursue,
Would run aground in coastal swell.

Bruno guessed the plan at once.
It seemed that they were coastal-bound
Where razor reefs and unseen shoals
Could see them driven fast aground.
He therefore went below the decks
And locked his cabin door behind
And, lying in his hammock there,
He tried to bring old friends to mind.

And in his thoughts, he spoke to them.
He'd tried his best – succeeded too:
He'd saved the life of one betrayed
Just as they'd asked that he should do.
They also bade him tend the poor
And give great wealth away. At last
The chance to do these things had come,
But now was slipping from his grasp.

"I've learned my lesson. Hear me now
For with your help I'll yet succeed.
Bring your boats, and turn him back
And help me in my hour of need!"
Deep down, he thought they wouldn't come.
He stood, then shook his head and sighed
Whilst at that moment, close at hand,
A fearsome sight met Morgan's eyes.

Mad Dog Morgan stood there stunned.
The sky was clear. The sunlight blazed.
Yet up ahead despite the wind
There seemed to come a growing haze.
In minutes, banks of fog built up
And from it – filling him with fear –
Twelve ghostly masts and sails arose
And under them, twelve boats appeared.

They left no wake and made no noise.
Their ghostly timbers glowing pale,
They seemed to float above the waves
And moved with ease against the gale.
And at the bow of every boat,
A fishing captain gazed ahead
His arm outstretched accusingly.
There was no choice. Lord Morgan fled.

IV
BRUNO'S LOSS

THE CREW THOUGHT Morgan truly mad –
His words and actions quite absurd.
He said that he could "hear the dog" –
A noise not one of them had heard.
Quite why they fled, they couldn't see,
For normally he'd stand and fight,
But from this shabby English crew
He'd quaked with fear and taken flight!

He'd set one course, then change his mind:
The reasoning was hard to tell.
And now he'd swung towards the *Tern*
– And sailed into the wind, as well!
He screamed that they must "get away"
But what had caused him such alarm?
For miles around was empty sea
With nothing there to cause him harm . . .

The pirates, now, had had enough.
Lord Morgan had gone barking mad!
So while he struggled at the wheel
They gathered up what things they had
And crept away to make escape:
They dropped the longboat off the stern
Then leaped aboard and rowed away
From Mad Dog and *The Arctic Tern*.

So now, alone, Lord Morgan sailed,
And with each hour, frustration grew.
Curses on *The Arctic Tern!*
And curses on those twelve ships too!
For if he turned, old Bruno's boat
Would spot this, and would alter course.
And if he went the other way,
Those ghostly ships would head him off.

There thus was little he could do:
He couldn't even set a course.
The way he went was not his choice:
And every turn he made was forced.
But still, alone behind the wheel
He struggled on with little sleep.
He'd suffer anything at all –
Would rather die than face defeat.

Aboard *The Arctic Tern*, the men
Were jubilant with their success:
The North-West course on which they sailed
Was one which would retrace their steps!
If all went well, they'd soon be home
And like a sheepdog with a flock,
They guide Lord Morgan all the way
Until they'd moored in Plymouth docks.

And so it was, some two days on
As midday sun beat all around
That Morgan and *The Arctic Tern*
Approached the edge of Plymouth Sound.
For all those miles the wind had howled
But as they came to Renne's Rocks
And neared the Shagstone, suddenly
The gale-force wind abruptly dropped.

Exhausted, hanging from the wheel,
Lord Morgan gazed in disbelief
As to one side, the ghostly ships
Sailed on towards the rocky reef.
And as he stared, the vessels seemed
To slowly melt beneath the sun.
The masts dissolved – so too the mist:
The ships all gone . . . except for one.

For to the port, *The Arctic Tern*
Rolled slowly as she lay becalmed.
So far away, without a breeze,
At least she couldn't cause him harm.
But as he watched, he shook his head:
For as each wave came rolling in
It carried Bruno's boat along
And drove it ever nearer him.

Old Bruno sighed. At last they'd won.
And as the ships and ghostly haze
Evaporated, so he felt
The tension of those recent days
Lift from his shoulders. Now he stood
And watched as gentle waves and tide
Licked their timbers, washed them gently
On towards Lord Morgan's side.

Adrian released the sails
And walked with Bruno to the bow.
Doctor Chris, and Hunter too,
Now surfaced from their bunks below.
The doctor took a grappling hook
And from his belt he hung his sword,
Prepared to hook Lord Morgan's boat
Then pull it in and go aboard.

Lord Morgan knew the game was up,
But even so, he'd make quite sure
That if he couldn't win this fight,
The treasure chest would stay aboard.
He climbed the mast, and raised a flag:
And where the Jolly Roger flew
The octopus with fiery eyes
Upon a flag now hung there too.

He went below and took an axe
And sharpened up its blade of steel
then swung it down repeatedly
And smashed a hole beside the keel.
As icy water flooded in,
He climbed the stairs to reach the deck
And stood beside the treasure chest –
Trapped now aboard a sinking wreck.

With Dolly parrot on his arm
He stood beside the bronze ship's bell
And shouted to *The Arctic Tern*,
"You'll only catch me now in Hell!
You thought that treasure would be yours:
Would soon be split between the crew.
Well, bad luck! I've got news for you!
If I can't have it, nor can you!"

They watched aghast as Morgan's boat
Now settled, and the upper decks
Were covered by the gentle waves
Which shortly climbed to Morgan's neck.
He glared at Bruno to the last,
And uttered not a single word.
In seconds now, the ship had gone:
The pirate flags the last submerged.

And as they watched they saw the parrot
Flap her wings and start to fly.
And from the waves she launched aloft
And rose into the clear blue sky.
She flew towards *The Arctic Tern*
And screeched and circled in the sun,
Screaming at her master's loss . . .
Then in a blur of green . . . was gone.

As Morgan's body was engulfed,
The water boiled about his face
And in the glare as Bruno watched
A transformation now took place.
Two fiery eyes glared out in red:
Eight tentacles seemed to appear;
An octopus writhed at the spot
There in the foam . . . then disappeared.

The Arctic Tern limped to the shore.
Her crew would have a tale to tell:
Of pirates, treachery and death:
Of castles, kings and gold as well.
But Bruno stood alone awhile.
He'd lost. And who knew if, or when,
That chance "to give great wealth away"
Would ever come to him again?

V
HOME AT LAST

THAT EVENING, ashore, a huge party was held
With a corner reserved at their pub "The McBride".
At the head of the table sat Bruno. As usual,
His coat had been placed on the floor by his side.
He ate his black rye-bread, fresh baked just that day,
And he supped from a tankard while facing the door
Never leaving a drop in his glass or his bottle
(In fact, in the way that I've told you before).

Next day, in a carriage, they travelled to London –
Were met by Royal guards, and were led to the court
Where they bowed to the Queen and, before her advisors,
Lord Hunter arose and then gave his report.
He spoke of Lord Morgan, and of his foul efforts
To murder the king and himself take the throne:
How Chris, as their doctor, had saved the king's life:
How the credit for this should be Chris's alone.

He told her how Adrian slept in the kitchens –
Discovered how Morgan concealed poisoned wine:
How, confronted, Lord Morgan had pulled out a dagger,
How Daisy had hung from his arm just in time.
They said that the merciful king had recovered:
The tale of the trial was then faithfully told:
How the king had insisted they take back to England
A treasure chest crammed with both silver and gold.

And finally, Hunter explained how the treasure
Was stolen by Morgan not five days before.
How *The Arctic Tern* chased him and (this bit was odd)
Had been able to steer him towards English shores.
They told how, at last, Morgan knew he was beaten
And scuppered the ship near the shore, off a reef
Known as 'Renne's Rocks' then (just as now) to the locals:
How the Shagstone now marked where the ship came to grief.

The tale of adventure was ended. A silence
Descended on all who stood there in the court.
Lord Hunter stepped forward, then knelt by the Queen
And delivered the scroll of pale parchment he'd brought.
And in it, the king said he might not have trusted
Ambassadors, messengers . . . men of that kind.
But these were unlike any men he had known.
It was through their compassion this treaty was signed.

The Queen was delighted. Her faith was rewarded.
At last! Peace with Spain! And to her it was clear
That the credit for this was not hers, but belonged
To the men (and the dog!) who were now standing here.
She drew Hunter's sword bade them kneel, dubbed their shoulders:
"Arise now, brave knight!" she then said to each man.
(In fact, they were now knights of Spain and of England –
This record in honour is one which still stands).

Doctor Chris went to Oxford, where Jenny his wife
Had been patiently waiting for him to return.
He was greeted with joy by his two little girls,
Both delighted to hear of the honours he'd earned.
The rest of his life he devoted to science
And never again did he go back to sea.
Jenny's business expanded with 'By Royal Appointment'
The label she tied to her fine jewelry.

Adrian went back to Bridget his wife,
And in Rolvenden opened a place serving food:
He would cook it himself, and the customers came
For the freshly baked rye-bread, and ale he had brewed.
He lived out his days in this sleepy Kent village –
The restaurant stood only yards from the green.
If you go there, you'll find that the green still remains
And that Adrian's place (now a pub) is still seen.

Lord Hunter went home to Louise in the North,
And without hesitation, he begged for her hand.
They were married that month in a grand church in Durham;
The reception which followed was just as they planned.
And it has to be said that the party was good,
For both Steve and Louise were awake at the dawn.
They lived in the castle where, just nine months later,
Their first son, a boy they called Daniel, was born.

Old Bruno went back to his fishing in Plymouth,
Where all of the locals were worried to see
How depressed he'd become since returning from Spain,
And how lonely and weary he now seemed to be.
He no longer went far – cast his nets out in Heybrook.
If asked, he would say he had only one wish:
He was fishing for timber of some sunken boat
And was hoping to catch silver coins and not fish . . .

The decades went by, and the young became old –
Just Old Bruno, his boat, and old Daisy remained.
The passage of time, though did not seem to mark them:
One hundred years on, you'd have noticed no change.
And each evening, you'd find him alone in the pub.
If you asked him for what he was waiting that day
He'd look up from his pint, and would say, "For the chance
To recover fortune, then give it away."

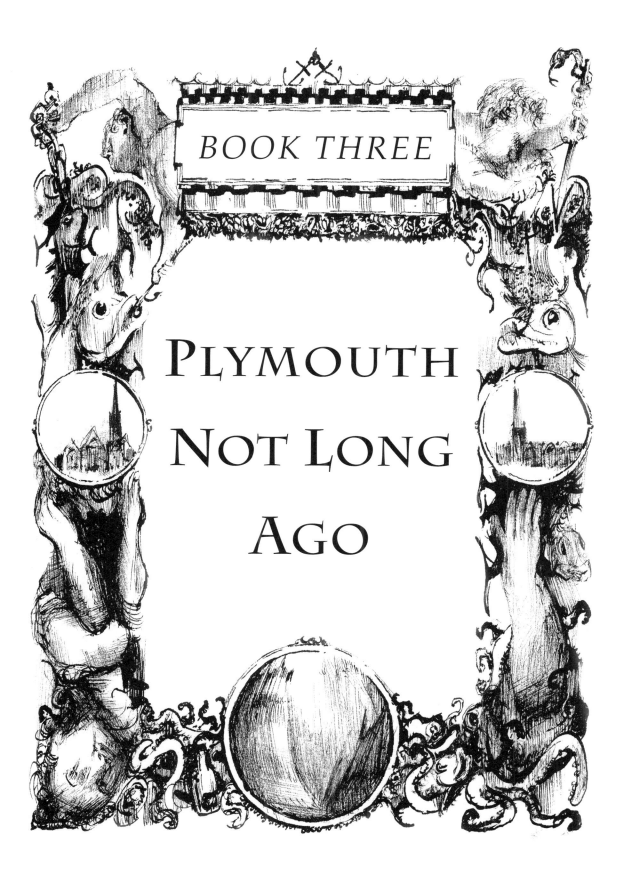

BOOK THREE

PLYMOUTH

NOT LONG

AGO

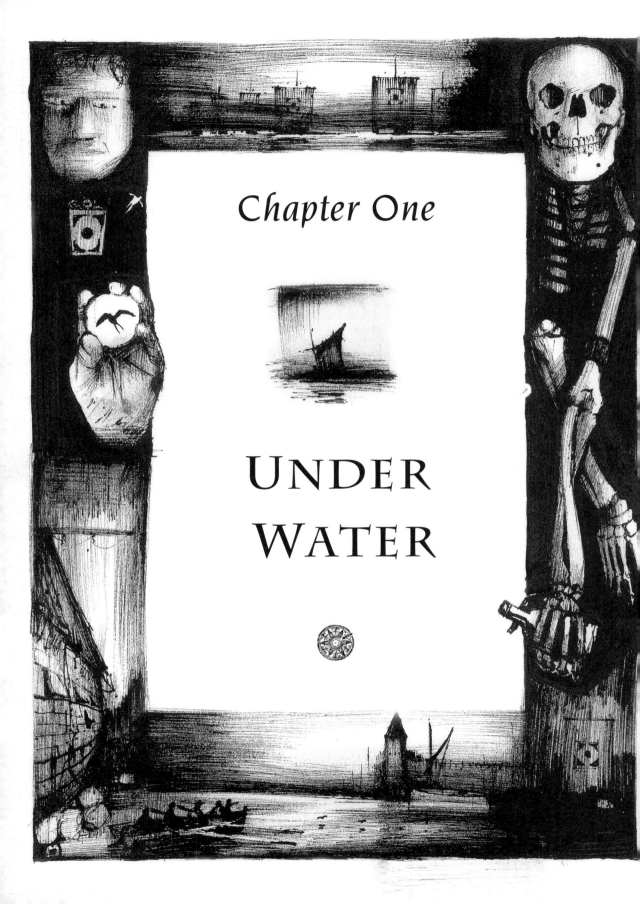

Chapter One

UNDER WATER

I
A Brief History
of Diving

FOR CENTURIES, mankind has tried
To swim beneath the waves and find
The treasures which he thinks must be
Beneath the surface of the sea.
In early days, he'd take a reed
(One hollowed out so he could breathe)
And in his mouth he'd hold it tight
And hope that in this way he might
Draw breath while swimming on some reef:
The tip above – his face beneath.

Still others tried to hold their breath
And, wearing flippers, plumb the depths
Until they'd have to make their way
From ocean gloom to light of day.
They ever deeper sought to go,
And sometimes carried weights below
To take them down with greater speed:
And in this way, aimed to succeed
In going deeper than before
With every venture from the shore.

Still others, weighted down with lead,
Put household buckets on their heads!
(The buckets had been modified
Specifically that they might dive:
With rope to hold them, and glass too
To help them take a submerged view.)
These home-made efforts, made of wood,
Thus formed a sort of makeshift hood
Whose air supply was pretty small.
With leaks, they weren't much use at all.

The same idea was later tried
With barrels lowered from the side
Of boats, from which old wrecks were sought
Wherein lay treasures (so they thought).
The weighted barrel would descend,
And from the barrel's open end
A diver could appear and swim:
When out of breath he'd go back in.
Pumped through a hose, fresh air would go
From boat to barrel down below.

Two men (the Deans) had some success
In salvaging great wealth from wrecks
And in the eighteenth century
They salvaged cannon from the seas.
They used a barrel and airhose
To dive a wreck – *The Mary Rose.*
With modern gear, the wreck was raised
And now, in Portsmouth, is displayed.
But with the cannon there on show
Are those the Deans brought from below.

It took two hundred years or more
Of trial, mistakes, and deaths before
Two men, called Cousteau and Gagnan,
Designed an early aqualung.
They tried it first in open sea
In France (in nineteen forty-three)
And using it they quickly found
That they could dive and swim around
And breathe through valves from tanks of air
Which, on their backs, they'd carried there.

With copied tanks and valves like these,
Still others found that they could breathe
And swim for hours quite happily
Beneath the surface of the sea.
They used it just for fun or sport
Until to some there came the thought
That with it they could salvage wrecks
And search for treasure, swim the decks
Of ships which lay beyond the reach
Of any land-bound man or beast.

II
THE DIVER

IN PLYMOUTH was a man like this
Who'd made his living catching fish.
He'd lived there all his life – had been
A feature of the local scene
For longer than most could recall:
Known and loved by one and all.

In summer nineteen sixty-one,
He'd bought an early aqualung:
A rubber wet suit, all in black,
With tanks to go upon his back.
Within a week or maybe two
He'd got the hang of what to do
And took to spending all free time
Indulging in his new pastime.

He trawled that winter, but next year
Abandoned nets and fishing gear.
Instead, he kitted out his boat
With winches, hooks and miles of rope
Thereafter spending every day
In diving kit 'round Heybrook Bay.

Each summer day, he'd walk along
The cobbles of the Barbican
And stop down by the waterside,
And in "The Admiral McBride"
He'd sit and drink a pint of ale,
Eat fresh-baked bread. He'd then set sail
And hug the coast while running East
Past Bovisand and Wembury beach.

The local people saw that he
Would always, when he put to sea,
Head straightaway for Renne's Rocks
And once nearby, prepare to drop
A length of rope to which was tied
An anchor with, hitched to its side,
A sack from which three more ropes came
Each ten yards long, and just the same.

With aqualung upon his back,
He'd dive below to where the sack
Of which you've heard me speak before
Hung inches from the ocean floor.
And then along a length of rope
(One of the three of which I spoke)
He'd swim until he reached the tip
Which dragged, of course, behind the ship.

Abandoned to the wind and tide
(The fisherman now off the side),
The boat would drift along and tow
The man along, who far below
Had passed the sack beneath the ship
And to a rope had taken grip.

The fisherman would therefore scour
The seabed in each waking hour
And in this way could search with ease
A vast expanse beneath the seas
Where metal scrap, dumped in the War,
Lay littering the ocean floor.
For bombs and wire and metal plate
And engine parts all met this fate:
In wartime all this waste was tipped
Straight overboard from fighting ships.

Some scrap like this was worth a bomb
(If you'll excuse an awful pun):
For iron, he cared not a jot,
But brass or lead was worth a lot.
Such metal, shining white or gold,
He'd spot and salvage to be sold.
He'd lift the piece, then swim right back
And dump it in the nearby sack.

And when the sack at last was full
He'd surface, clamber out, and pull
On winches till at last he'd see
The load appear, all draped in weed.
He'd lower it upon the deck
Would tip it out, and then inspect
The haul, and shortly he'd dump overboard
The worthless bits, and keep a hoard
Of metals he might sell, instead:
(Like brass and bronze and tin and lead.)

The scrap, when sold, made just enough
To keep the boat and buy his crust,
But never would he be as rich
As if he'd stuck to catching fish.
In fact, as all the locals saw,
This diving lark had made him poor:
He wore old clothes, could not afford
A place to live, so slept on board.

The locals had no sympathy
When each day he put out to sea:
They'd grumble – could be heard to say
That if he went to Heybrook Bay
And never ever made a start
On salvaging in different parts
Then he could only blame himself
For his continued lack of wealth.

And sometimes they would ask him why
He didn't make a change, and try
To salvage somewhere else one day?
It might be that, not far away,
Ten tons of brass lay all around
In piles which cried out to be found?
It seemed quite clear: in Heybrook Bay
There wasn't much left anyway.
If they were him, that's what they'd choose.
What had he, anyway, to lose?

He'd thank them for their sound advice:
It really was so very nice
That people should be so concerned
About how little he now earned.
They might be right, then, to suggest
That hunting elsewhere would be best.
For now, he'd carry on this way
And make no changes to his day.
He'd have his pint, then leave the docks
And search the reefs round Renne's Rocks.

This obstinacy made them mad.
He seemed content with what he had!
Despite their help, he seemed to be
Content to live in poverty!
Well, that was that. They'd had a try.
The bed he'd made was where he'd lie!

Just one or two, though, thought that he
Was not as stupid as he seemed.
Perhaps he had another plan
(One not divulged to any man)
And wasn't seeking brass or lead
But rather something else instead?
Maybe he wasn't after scrap
But rather had a secret map
Which showed him that great treasure lay
Upon the reef near Heybrook Bay?

They'd sometimes tease him, buy him beer
Then sit and chat and bend his ear:
Each day, they'd ask, when leaving port,
Was it only scrap he sought?
He then might look them in the eye
And might, as if to make reply,
Hold their gaze a little while
And gently shake his head . . . and smile . . .

The years went by, and little changed
Though some who noticed thought it strange
That even now, he'd still be found
Out searching that same hunting ground.
With passing years, they all felt sure
He looked no older than before.

Now, over time it's my belief
That fate will always crush the thief:
And you will almost always find
That good will triumph, given time.
The fisherman, though, needed help,
Were he to find, amidst the kelp,
The wreck and chest, if they remained
And if they were to be regained . . .

III
HELP ARRIVES

IN SPRING OF nineteen sixty-eight
(I can't recall the exact date)
And in a village now called Drayton
(Not far at all from Didcot station)
A doctor bought an old stone barn
Which once housed cattle on a farm.
And here, he planned to spend his life
With his two daughters and his wife.

He worked amongst the dreaming spires
Of Oxford, home of gowns and choirs,
Researching what made people tick,
And what went wrong to make them sick.
He loved his work, but secretly
He sought the opportunity
To leave, and start his life anew.
He knew exactly what he'd do:
He'd move the family away
To live in some secluded bay.
The girls would have a beach to comb
With shells to find and bring back home,
While he, the happiest man alive
Would go off every day and dive.

The doctor's wife knew of his plans.
For in the time she'd known this man
He must have surely dived on most
Of all the sites round Britain's coast?

One morning, as he rose from bed,
He glanced towards his wife, and said
That he'd been thinking. Maybe they
Might take a fortnight's holiday?
He'd thought that Plymouth might be good.
They'd walk on Dartmoor, eat good food,
And if in search of things to do . . .
. . . Perhaps he'd do some diving too?

She laughed. She'd like a holiday –
Enjoy the chance to get away
From work and home tasks for a while
But really! She just had to smile,
For when he told her of the plan,
He made it sound as if dry land
Was where he planned, most days, to be
And not, in fact, beneath the sea!

She did, however, briefly pause
To wonder what on earth had caused
Her husband to so suddenly
Propose this trip down to the sea?
He hadn't mentioned it before,
Nor talked of Plymouth, she felt sure.
But never mind. This short break should
Do all of them the world of good.

In fact, her husband didn't dare
To tell her what the true facts were
For fear that she might think him mad
For acting in the way he had.
Last night, he'd not long been in bed
And, tired, was sleeping like the dead
When vividly, he had a dream:
He saw a Plymouth harbour scene.
And in his mind's eye, he could see
A weathered vessel by a quay
And on the deck of salt-stained wood
An ancient fisherman now stood.

And as he dreamed, he felt quite sure
He'd met this sailor long before.
He couldn't match the bearded face
To any recent time or place,
Nor could he summon up a name . . .
. . . Though was there some strange link with Spain?
The sailor turned without a word
Then smiled, and beckoned him aboard.
Chris woke, and in that instant knew
Exactly what he had to do.
With haste, he had to make his way
To Plymouth for a holiday.

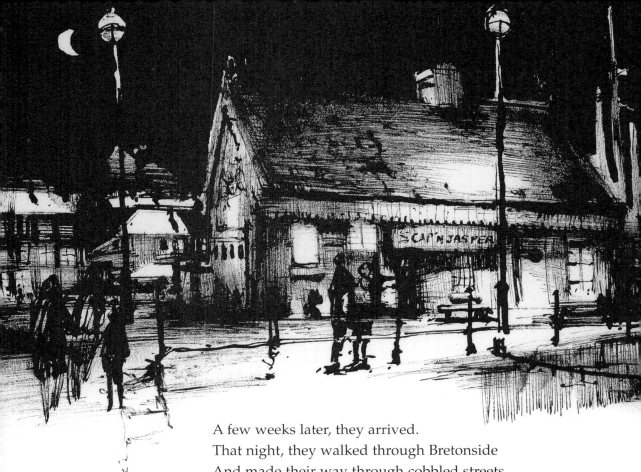

A few weeks later, they arrived.
That night, they walked through Bretonside
And made their way through cobbled streets
(The ones of which you've heard me speak).
And on the quay they spent some time
Examining a defused mine
Used for collections now, as then,
To pay for Britain's lifeboat men.

They bought a burger from a stall
Called "Cap'n Jasper's" – known to all
For serving food and mugs of tea
To all those folk who went to sea.
For many generations past
Had longed for Jasper's fine repast:
When back ashore from days at sea
There was no better place to be.

A little further on, there stood
That boat of burnished salt-stained wood
The doctor stared, for this boat seemed
Just like the one of which he'd dreamed.
He swore that when the morning came,
And if he then felt just the same,
He'd find the captain of the ship
And ask if he might take a trip.

And here, a pub he recognised:
Its name – "The Admiral McBride".
The doctor felt he knew it well
(Though how, he really couldn't tell)
And asked his wife if she would mind
If they should take a little time
And pop inside and have a beer –
And spend a quiet evening here?

Once inside the old oak door,
He looked across the wooden floor
And froze. His jaw dropped as he stared
For by a table, over there,
Was sat the fisherman he'd seen
Aboard the boat of which he'd dreamed.
His eyes were bright like burning coals
And seemed to look inside their souls.

A thick black beard lay in a pile
And in its midst, they saw a smile.
With folded sleeves, spread out with care
His jacket lay down by his chair.
And from the door, a trail of sand
Mixed in with salt led to the man.
Although they never could have met,
For them, it seemed, a place was set.

For round the table were four chairs.
In front of each, a meal prepared:
Fresh bread and – really, this was strange –
A fresh-pulled pint of foaming ale.
He stood. "How very fine it is
To meet again, my Doctor Chris.
Dear Jenny! We've not met before.
And girls! A pleasure I am sure!".

"Please, take a seat. You must be tired
After such a lengthy drive.
From here to Oxford, I must say,
Is quite a distance for one day.
The others shouldn't be too long:
In fact, unless I'm very wrong
They'll get here in an hour or so
(They haven't got so far to go)."

The doctor's wife now laughed aloud.
"I never ever will allow
This man to trick me in this way!
He told me that this holiday
Was not one of his diving trips –
And now I find these friends of his!
A family trip? Boy! Was I wrong!
You'd planned some diving all along!"

The doctor sat there, taking stock.
He felt quite faint. Completely shocked.
He looked around. Were they on film?
Were hidden cameras watching him?
In truth, he felt he knew this chap
Relaxing in his captain's cap.
For meetings, though, he'd had no plans
With this or any other man.

And more. How could this man have known
Where he and Jenny had their home?
He must have sensed when they'd arrive
To get fresh beer put on the side.
The captain thought that men he knew
Would shortly be arriving too
As if this meeting had been set
With others whom he'd never met!

Now, past "The Admiral McBride"
A surgeon wandered just outside.
He worked in London, but today
Had travelled down to holiday
In Plymouth. He, too, didn't know
Quite what had made him want to go.
Perhaps it was that vivid dream
Which just last month had come to him?

In any case, one thing was clear:
He'd get to do some diving here.
He'd tried it once some years before,
But only gone in from the shore.
But now, he planned to get afloat,
And do some diving from a boat.
He saw the pub. Perhaps he'd find
The skipper of a boat inside?

He wandered in, and there ahead
He saw a table had been set.
Around, a group of people sat –
And one had on a captain's cap.
He made his way towards the group:
The captain, smiling, turned and stood
And called him over. "Take a seat!
So, Hunter, once again we meet!"

The same confusion filled his head
As that which Doctor Chris had felt.
It also struck a restaurateur
Who shortly walked in through the door.
The latter, who'd come down from Kent,
Had also had a dream which sent
Him off to pack his things and drive
To Plymouth, where he hoped to dive.

The three men there each thought it rude
To go, or leave the beer and food
So sat and chatted. Found it strange
That they all knew each other's names.
They had the sort of ease you find
With those who know each other's minds:
In fact, as if they'd somehow known
Each other some time long ago.

In conversation, it was clear
That something odd had brought them here.
Yet none of them now felt alarmed –
The others clearly meant no harm
And each of them, they all now knew,
Was also trained in diving, too,
And each had planned to find a way
To do some in the coming days.

Tomorrow, they would have to meet.
At nine, they'd gather in the street
And see if they could find afloat
Some dinghy or some fishing boat
Whose captain might agree to show
The three of them some place to go
Where they might don their kit and try
To get some safe and scenic dives.

Till now, the captain wasn't heard
(In fact, he'd hardly said a word),
But at this point, he stood and spoke:
He was the skipper of a boat
And had it moored not far from here,
All kitted out with diving gear.
Perhaps they'd like to come next day
And dive with him in Heybrook Bay?

The deal was done. What luck they'd had!
You know, this really wasn't bad!
To find fine friends, fine beer and food
And now a boat! Yes! This was good!
And, strangely, not a single one
Now seemed to know just how they'd come
To meet each other. No . . . not clear
Quite how it was they'd all met here . . .
  . . . The memory of dreams and such . . .
Had blown away . . .
  . . . Like
    . . . So much
      . . . Dust . . .

IV
DIVING TOGETHER

NEXT DAY, as arranged, they all met by the quay.
They had not brought their weightbelts or tanks full of air,
For the captain had told them he'd long had things ready,
And once on the boat they'd find everything there.
A new valve to breathe with, and mask, fins and snorkle,
A knife and a wetsuit for each, made to fit,
Would be laid out on bunks in the berths he'd prepared
With a clean canvas bag which would hold their new kit.

The sight of the vessel left Hunter disturbed,
For he thought that he knew her from some time before . . .
How strange he should think this – and how strange as well
That he pictured her moored by some far Spanish shore.
Puzzled, he gazed at her burnished brown timbers
And bow, where he noticed a few peeling words –
Inscribed in old paintwork the words *Arctic Tern*
And beneath them was painted a black and white bird.

The boat leaped with joy as they sailed from the harbour –
And fish, near the bow, skipped on spume 'neath bright skies
As Daisy stood sniffing the sharp salty spray
With her fur blown in great woollen waves from her eyes.
As they sailed out past Bovisand, on to the Shagstone
Old Bruno told how they would gather up scrap:
They'd swim up the line (which was towed by the vessel)
To put all the pieces they had in a sack.

On reaching the Shagstone, he lowered the anchor:
Attached were three ropes which then drifted behind.
The engines were cut, and they put on their kit.
They pulled down their masks and flopped over the side.
The cool Plymouth waters seeped in through their wetsuits
And chilled them as, headfirst, they sank deep below.
They swam to the end of a rope as they drifted
And, searching for scrap, they then swam to and fro.

They had a great time – filled the sack, in one day,
With more scrap than the fisherman ever achieved,
But despite their success, and the money it meant,
The captain was not really happy, it seemed.
He said he was pleased with the metal they'd found,
But was saddened their searches had not yet revealed
Any timbers or, maybe, an old rusting anchor —
The signs of a wreck which had long being concealed.

Next day (and the ones for the rest of the week)
Were successful in terms of the metal they found.
But, search as they might through the weeds on the reefs,
They still couldn't see any wreckage around.
At night, they would gather to drink in the pub
And relax, and proclaim how they all were so glad
To have come on this trip, to have met these new friends:
And what excellent diving each day they had had.

A week soon went by with the crew in good spirit.
The captain grew sadder, though, each day they sailed.
It wasn't their fault. How, indeed, could they know
What the future would hold for him if their search failed?
As Saturday's dinner was served in the pub
He decided he had little choice, and that night
He would ask them to stay as he told them a tale
Of a captain they knew, and his desperate plight.

They did as he asked, and when all were replete
He sat forward, then steadily gazed at each one.
They solemnly settled in silence to hear him:
The customers quietened. A tale was to come.
Those standing nearby edged in closer to hear him –
A shuffling circle, three deep, round the man.
He'd never before let these people so near.
In this static suspense, he drew breath. And began . . .

"They call it a legend," he said, "and round here
There are many who first heard the tale in their youth.
But like small grains of sand in the middle of pearls
You may find in a legend a small grain of truth.
In fact, I assure you, this isn't a legend.
At first, you'll be startled by what you have heard.
Believe me, however – I have inside knowledge –
The story is true, down to every last word."

"A man may cause hurt to the people around him:
In numerous ways may he cause them such pain.
He may steal from their homes. He may lie or may cheat.
He may wait till they're down, and then kick them again.
Their anguish will always be many times worse:
And their fury is sure to be far multiplied
If they find that the person who did all these things
Was a man who once stood as a friend by their side."

"Far North, many thousands of years in the past,
Was a man known as Mad Dog, who lived such a life.
He would steal and would plunder for no better reason
Than for his enjoyment of pain and of strife.
He looked at the fishermen casting their nets
And he envied their happiness, vowing he'd try
To bring sorrow to all of these men and their folks
And would wipe out their village which nestled nearby.

"He sought out a man who, though simple, was greedy:
And found it quite easy to purchase the fool.
In seconds the man had agreed to the deal.
He'd sell out all his friends in return for some jewels.
The Mad Dog was happy to watch this betrayal:
His pleasure would surely be well worth the pay.
Indeed, some months later, he stood there and gloated:
All villagers dead, bar the traitor, that day.

"Forgiveness is hard, for your instinct is always
To hate anybody who's done you some harm
But harder than this is to see your own guilt
And forgive yourself all of the things you've done wrong.
The fisherman knew that his actions were evil –
Was ridden with guilt and decided one day
That he couldn't forgive himself what he had done –
So he set out to drown himself off Wembury Bay.

"Now sometimes the people who've suffered a crime
Cannot stand the injustice and, restless, they try
To seek out their assailant and make him see reason:
Such battles may go on long after they've died.
The ghosts of the fishermen killed by their friend
Were united to fight till their battle was won.
They came to their friend, and explained he'd not rest
Till his wrongs were all righted, and justice was done.

"(I explained all these things to a playwright one day
– Name of William something – I knew I'd forget –
Had a place down in Stratford-on-Avon, I think.
Got quite famous, they say, not long after we'd met.
He said he believed me, and mentioned these things
In a play he was writing about one betrayed.
It concerned some chaps 'Brutus', and 'Julius Caesar',
And showed that wrongdoings live after the grave.)

"This mission entrusted, the fisherman waited –
For many long years he resided nearby.
Each moment he lived he would try to do good,
And put right all those wrongs, that he might one day die.
He failed in these efforts – had little success,
But he hoped beyond hope that he might find some way
Not to take, but to save some betrayed person's life
And receive some great wealth, and then give it away.

"Now some centuries later, he spotted his chance
To do all of these things, and thus travelled to Spain.
There he found that the Mad Dog had never faced justice:
The evil man's soul had appeared once again.
The fisherman won, with the aid of some friends
Who all vowed that they'd help him again if they could.
They swore their allegiance. If ever he sought them
They'd answer his call, come at once if they could.

"As it happened, the victory in Spain was not total.
Although he had managed to save one betrayed
And had gathered great wealth, he had failed at the last:
All the wealth he'd received he'd not given away.
It remained undisturbed – a great mountain of treasure –
He knew where the chest which contained it still lay.
It was out near the Shagstone, just where they'd been diving:
A fortune in silver piled up in the Bay.

"I have searched for this treasure for years with no luck.
And it lies where it sank on a boat 'neath the sea.
If I find it, I plan not to keep it at all,
For the man in the tale is a man known to me.
And that fisherman now has grown weary of waiting.
The treasure, once found, will all go to the poor:
He'll at last join the villagers he'd once betrayed:
Shed his burden of guilt. Rest in peace. Strive no more."

The story was told, and he drew on his ale
As the customers silently walked to the door.
Within a few minutes, they sat there alone –
Just the captain and friends in that pub by the shore.
He slowly stood up, said "Goodnight, one and all.
Let us now leave for bed. May you sleep well tonight,
For tomorrow we gather at dawn one more time
In our efforts to ease that poor fisherman's plight."

V
Leaving Port

IN THE MORNING, they met on the ancient stone cobbles
Where trawlers still came, and where still you could buy
Cooked fish from a stall which they called "Cap'n Jasper's"
Though no-one around could remember quite why.
From the baker's shop (Jago's) they bought some crisp loaves
And the four of them noticed how strange all this seemed,
For the smells and the places all seemed quite familiar,
As if they were visited once in a dream.

They rounded the headland with Chris at the bow
Staring out at the Shagstone, and trying his best
To look out for a clue (though he didn't know what)
Which might guide him to finding that old treasure chest.
As he looked at the wavetops, he thought that he glimpsed
Some green bird, now and then, in the midst of the swell.
Had he seen it before? He felt sure that he had
Although where this had been, he could no longer tell.

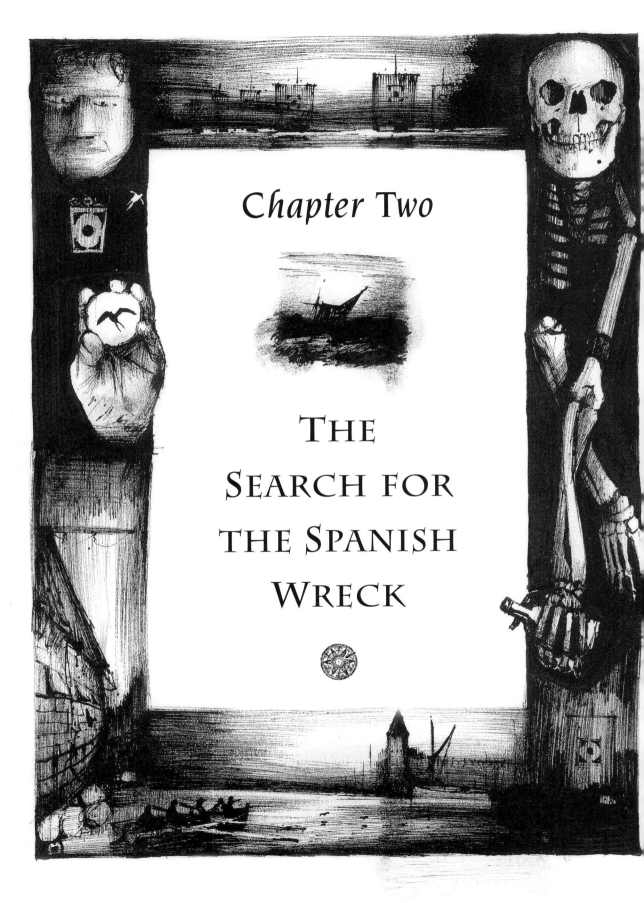

Chapter Two

The
Search for
the Spanish
Wreck

I
THE WRECK DISCOVERED

THE BOAT FORGED on through ice-blue waters,
The warming sun was climbing now,
And brilliant beams bounced off the drops
Which splintered from the thrusting bow.
She surfed the crests of gentle waves
And joyfully she made her way
Through friendly waters past the point
Then cut a line towards the Bay.

And now they came to Renne's Rocks.
Up in the bow, there stood the crew
All looking keenly round about
(Accompanied by Daisy too).
They'd listened hard the night before
To what the captain said to do.
To find the wreck of which they'd heard
They'd search the shore and sea for clues.

The captain cut the engines now.
The Arctic Tern rocked peacefully
With gentle creaking from the decks
Adrift upon a glassy sea.
The sparkling sea, the burning sun,
And squinting at the coast and skies
Caused the surgeon's head to ache
So for a while, he shut his eyes.

From random patterns which appeared
A shape in grey was slowly born.
At first, it swirled like rolling mist,
But gradually, it took on form.
A beak appeared. A tiny head,
And graceful wings all came in turn.
He'd seen this image on the bow:
This was, he knew, an Arctic tern.

And as he watched, with eyes still shut,
The bird took flight and seemed to soar
Above some ancient Spanish ship.
He'd surely seen all this before?
And listening now, he heard a voice
Come drifting in across the sea.
It startled him to know her name:
The woman speaking was "Louise".

She told him that the bird he'd seen
Was sent by her: that it would show
The fisherman and all his friends
Precisely where they ought to go.
With that, his vision disappeared
The image fading like her words.
He opened both his eyes again
And saw – right there – the self-same bird!

The others also saw it too:
It wheeled before them in the skies
And as the surgeon first had found,
The bird was one they recognised.
The captain stared, then ran at once
To fire the engines, for he knew
They'd find the boat they sought once more
By following where'er she flew.

And as the bird now turned to shore
The boat (her namesake) followed suit
The captain copied every move –
Precisely following her route.
And if she flew ahead too fast,
The crew aboard would quickly find
That she would circle for a while
Ensuring they'd not fall behind.

They tacked and turned for quite some time
(And to the fisherman it seemed
She'd lost the wreck – could not recall
Quite where the sinking boat had been.)
Then suddenly she seemed to pause
And, hovering, let out a cry.
She swooped – then soaring at the sun
Was lost within the burning sky.

The captain knew the wreck was close
And swiftly, now, he marked the spot
By dropping, from the stern, a buoy
He'd tied onto a weighted shot.
And from the stern, he hung the anchor,
Measured, as they'd done before,
To hang beneath *The Arctic Tern*
Three feet above the ocean's floor.

He called the crew: explained the search.
They'd slowly motor up and down
Until the anchor snagged below:
In this way would the wreck be found.
They took their places quickly now,
And minutes later were prepared.
The engines fired, and they were off!
The wreck, in no time, would be theirs!

He fired the engines up at once
And, gently now, he turned the boat.
He took a bearing on the shore,
As now the bow brushed past the float.
He'd planned to search for many hours
But all at once, the line went taut . . .
The boat had travelled not two yards –
Before her anchor had been caught!

The captain seized the line at once.
The crew, with great excitement, stood
And watched the captain haul it in.
Stuck to the anchor flukes was . . . wood!
He sighed aloud – sank to his knees.
The ancient wreck in Plymouth Sound –
The one for which he'd searched these years –
Had, without doubt, this day been found!

They left the buoy to mark the site
And ran for home that afternoon.
They scarcely could believe their luck
That they had found the wreck so soon.
The captain, though, was more relieved:
For some, the search had scarce begun.
He'd spent much longer, though, than that:
For him, the search was lifetimes long.

II
DIVING THE WRECK

AT DAWN THE NEXT morning they gathered again
And set sail for the wreck which, not one day before,
Had been found by the crew of the old fishing ship
After centuries lying upon the sea floor.
The buoy was still there, in the place where they'd left it
(In fact, if you look from the shore, then you might
Catch a glimpse of it still: those that don't know the story
Assume it marks lobster pots left overnight).

Approaching now, slowly, the anchor once more
Had been hung from the stern till it caught in the wreck.
With their ship now positioned right over their prize,
The divers now busied themselves on the deck.
The captain had asked that the others go first:
Find the wreck, check its age, and then please look around
In an effort to find where the main deck had been
In the hope that the treasure chest might then be found.

They put on their wet suits, their masks, fins and snorkles,
Their bottles of air, and their valves and their gloves.
They dropped overboard, sinking fast through cool waters
And soon left the fishing boat far up above.
The water glowed green in bright sun from the surface,
All noise from the boat was blocked out as they went:
The hiss of sucked air and the gurgle and tinkle
Of bubbles alone could be heard in descent.

In minutes, they'd nearly completed their journey:
The shot line went straight to the anchor, they knew.
The anchor was fixed without doubt in the wreck
Which a shoal of large fish for a while blocked from view.
As they watched, the fish parted. Beneath them, they saw
Through the gloom, a shape forming amidst the green light.
As they sank down towards it, its form became clearer.
They froze as they met an extraordinary sight.

For there on the bottom was sitting a ship.
Not the battered old timbers they'd come to expect,
But a fully rigged vessel. An octopus pennant
With black skull and crossbones still flew from the wreck.
The sails were still hoisted. The cabin door open.
Some charts could be seen on a table inside.
All the fittings were brass, and were shining like new.
The wheel on the deck slowly spun in the tide.

They swam through the rigging, then paused: somewhere close
Came a slow mournful clanging which echoed around:
They followed the noise to the front of the wheel-house:
The ship's old brass bell was the source of the sound.
They turned from the bell and surveyed the main deck
Then, as one, all the divers drew in a sharp breath:
Right there, only yards away – lid tightly padlocked,
And strapped to the deck by old chains . . . lay a chest.

Finning gently, and carried along by the current,
They swam in a line through the green eerie gloom.
Their fins raised a mass of fine silt from the timbers
Like the dust blown from books in a long-empty room.
At the chest they discovered that both lock and chains
Had not rusted at all, but seemed almost brand new
And the leather which covered the wood glowed so brightly
It had surely been polished by some ghostly crew?

They did not pause long, but laid out all the tools
Which they'd carried in order to work on the wreck.
Using bolt-shears, the divers cut links from the chains,
Till at last, with a clank, they slipped down to the deck.
The chest had been freed. With a crowbar they carried
The lock on the front now came under attack:
With the bar through the hoop of the lock, they all heaved.
It creaked for a moment . . . then gave with a crack.

The divers thought hard about what they should do,
But it wasn't so easy to know what was best.
Should they lift the lid now, and perhaps find the riches?
Or go – let the fisherman open the chest?
Whatever they did, they must make haste about it
And reach their decision before not too long:
They'd been down for an age, and must go or risk drowning:
The air in their bottles was almost all gone.

On the surface, the fisherman waited and watched.
They'd been down on the bottom for ever, it seemed.
Had they found some old wreckage? And was it the ship
Which he'd sought every day, and at night filled his dreams?
At last, bubbles boiled on the shiny sea's surface,
Announcing that divers were soon to appear.
They bobbed to the surface, swam up to the side,
And then silently each of them handed him gear.

They hauled themselves out from the water at last,
And proceeded to clear up their kit without word.
The fisherman helped them to tidy it all,
But they said not a word till the kit was all stowed.
At last, Hunter faced him but still he said nothing.
– The tension was more than the sailor could stand.
His voice deep and shaking, he asked, "Did you find her?"
The answer: a Piece of Eight placed in his hand.

III
OLD ENEMIES

THE SIGHT OF the coin made the fisherman weep.
As he did so, he thanked them for all they had done.
Still, he said, there was yet one more step he must take
Were he ever to finish the trail he'd begun.
"My friend," he exclaimed, "you have given me freedom!
I love you, and thank you with all of my heart.
I shall miss you, but know there are things still to do.
We must say our goodbyes, for I soon shall depart."

"So, goodbye then to Hunter, my oldest of friends.
You should not be plain 'Hunter', but really a Lord.
You saved me this day, but some time in the past
It was I who saved you when I dragged you aboard.
And farewell young Adrian. Thank you again.
Though you might not remember our times on the seas,
You have helped me before in my quest to do good
And have always assisted and been true to me."

"Doctor Chris. Like the others, you share in the treasure.
You prove yourself worthy of high praise indeed.
To a king, many years in the past, you showed kindness.
This treasure, in part, was his thanks for those deeds.
The coins which you've brought to the surface are yours.
They will keep you all wealthy for decades to come.
There are few folk I'll miss. They all stand on this deck
And I've said my goodbyes to them all – except one."

He turned to old Daisy, who sat there and whimpered.
They looked at each other. He offered a smile
But she hung her head low, and slinked sadly towards him.
He knelt, took her paw, and then stroked her awhile.
"Farewell then, my friend. We have known one another
For longer than anyone here might believe.
I loved you more deeply than any companion.
Don't pine when I've gone. " He stood up. "I must leave."

With that, he got changed and once more donned his tank.
He paused at the side, took a last look around.
He would miss many things – the old ship and the pub,
And the swell and the spray as he sailed Plymouth Sound.
He took a deep breath, wiped his eyes with his hand,
Fixed his mask in position, and without more delay
Dropped over the side, gripped the line to the anchor.
With a splash of his fins, he was lost 'neath the waves.

Bruno sank through the gloom. He would have to be quick
For the tide had now turned and the current was strong.
The plankton was thick in the water around him –
A thick cloud of green as it floated along.
He sank ever deeper, and though the light dimmed,
He could make out a flag: in the strong current flow
It still billowed as once it had flown in a gale,
And still hung from the top of the mast far below.

Through rigging and sails he continued to sink,
As the sound of the bell (as they'd said) reached his ears.
Its dull eerie clanging grew louder and faster:
A warning to someone, perhaps, who lived here?
With quickening breaths, he swam on past the wheel-house
And up to the deck, where the chest should be found.
He searched the cold waters, then suddenly saw it!
It sat where it had when the ship had gone down!

The shackles and lock which had once strapped it down
Lay destroyed on the deck, where the divers had been.
The lid, though, was down . . . had the divers not told him
The lid was left UP? Or had that been a dream?
A cold shudder seized him. He wasn't alone.
He felt sure something evil was lurking nearby.
He anxiously glanced all around, seeing nothing
Then, eyes wide with horror, let out a short cry . . .

The lid on the chest had begun to creak open.
No hand could be seen to be doing this task
Yet it steadily rose, as coins spilled from the top
And then spun to the deck from the edge of the cask.
The treasures within were as he remembered,
With Pieces of Eight, by the thousand, inside:
Ten million pounds' worth of old Spanish coins
Now exposed, after hundreds of years, to the tide.

The lid now was up, yet he still couldn't tell
What had caused it to happen. He thought that, maybe,
It was merely the rush of the tide which had done it,
Or just a strong eddy, or swell from the sea?
But deep down he knew that it wasn't that simple.
An enemy lurked there (and one he must beat)
Who had stayed with the ship for these hundreds of years
And who'd waited that time to avenge his defeat.

The fisherman patiently studied the trunk
Till at last from around it, and just as he had feared,
A flicker of movement was glimpsed at each corner
And then, as he watched, some red flesh now appeared.
Eight tentacles writhed round the chest as the body,
All slimy and heaving and pulsing in size,
Sat amidst all the treasure, then turned round to face him:
An octopus glaring with fiery red eyes.

"We meet once again," thought the fisherman slowly,
"And still you are trying to get in my way!
I'd rather not fight, but will happily do so
In order that good shall beat evil this day.
I promised to right all my wrongs, and have done so
Except for one task which you know I have left:
I promised to seek out and seize a great fortune
And give it away, so that I can find rest."

He looked to his side, and reached down to his calf.
From a sheath which was strapped there, he pulled out a knife.
He gazed at the creature, now fixed with his stare:
"Get out of my way, if you value your life!"
The octopus, though, didn't move from the chest,
And its tentacles writhed and its red body glowed.
It was set on defending the chest to the last,
And drew strength from the fury the fisherman showed.

The diver went forward. His mind was made up.
He would kill the vile creature! The treasure was his!
Then all of a sudden, he thought of his friends
As they sailed their twelve boats through that strange ocean mist.
In those thousands of years, had he really not learned
That peace never was won if a man had to fight?
That no act born of hate or of violence brought good?
That the noblest of aims never made a wrong, right?

With that he looked down at the knife which he held.
Many years in the past, he'd had blood on these hands
As betrayal had led to the death of his friends
For a handful of jewels which were cast on the sand.
He let the knife drop. As he did so he sensed
That the creature was fearful to see him let go:
A man armed with hate and a knife may be dangerous:
A man armed with honour's a deadlier foe.

The fisherman slowly swam up to the chest.
He would claim what was his, and would set himself free.
He still had a promise he'd made to the poor
And he'd keep it.
He knew.
This was his destiny . . .

III
RESOLUTION

ABOVE, ON THE SURFACE, they'd watched as the captain
Had put on his gear and had said his goodbyes:
As he'd paused at the side, as his eyes scanned the sea:
As he took one last look at the bright Plymouth skies.
They were puzzled, but watched as he ducked through the waves
They had not understood what he'd meant – "I must go" –
But had followed the trail of the fine fizzing bubbles
Which had plotted the path that he took down below.

The bubbles had followed the fall of the shot line,
Then moved to the right as he followed the deck.
They paused for a moment – he must have now stopped
At the eerie dull clang of the bell on the wreck.
He set off again, and they thought of him making
His way past the wheel-house, and past the bell too.
Then they saw that the bubbles had once again stopped
And they knew he'd have paused as the chest came to view.

It was then that his actions seemed hard to explain,
For the path of the bubbles now didn't move on.
Was he caught in net? Had he run into trouble?
Just why was he sitting there? What had gone wrong?
Their worry increased, till at last they decided
To send down a diver to come to his aid.
As they made preparations, he set off again.
The final approach to the chest had been made.

As they stood there together, Lord Hunter looked up.
In the distance, he'd noticed the cry of a bird.
It was mournful and plaintive, and caught in the breeze,
Grew increasingly loud, until all the friends heard.
The call was unlike any other they knew,
So they turned, scanned the waves and then shielding their eyes,
They looked to the sun and the brightly lit clouds,
Where *The Arctic Tern*, high above, soared through the skies.

It came out of the sun, with its smooth agile wings
Flicking this way and that as they caught on the breeze.
It banked and it swooped, and then levelled its flight
Till it surfed through the spray which whipped up from the sea.
Approaching their boat, it gained height once again
And then banked round the mast as it circled the deck
With its eyes fixed below – not on them, but the bubbles
Which rose in a stream from the site of the wreck.

The bird was the same one which, not long before,
Had appeared and had led them to where the wreck lay.
But why had the bird, with its mission accomplished,
Come back to this place so late on in the day?
A sudden sharp wind gusted hard at the ship.
And from nowhere, dark clouds rose to blot out the sun.
A sense of foreboding surrounded the crew.
The bird was the herald of bad things to come . . .

Below, in the chest, the red octopus glowered
As four of its tentacles gripped the chest tight.
The other four rippled and writhed near the edge
Reaching out for the fisherman: ready to fight.
The diving knife, dropped by the fisherman, sparkled
And spun like speared fish as it spiralled to deck.
With both his hands empty, the fisherman came –
Kicking silt, as he swam, from the planks of the wreck.

He reached for the treasure – was suddenly seized
By a tentacle – first just by one, then by more.
He tried to pull back, but another coiled round him:
His arm was soon gripped by not three, but all four!
The tip of a tentacle inched round his neck
And its tightening grip made him dizzy with pain.
He tried with his fingers to prise the thing off
But the strength of the suckers meant all was in vain.

Two tentacles, soon, had been squeezed round his neck
And were hauling his head ever closer. In fright
He looked up at the octopus – saw its head tilted:
Its sharp evil beak had been opened to bite!
He wedged both his knees on the side of the chest:
But the strength of the creature was more than a match:
The octopus seemed to be reeling him in:
He wasn't a fisherman now, but the catch!

His head was just inches away from the jaws
When he reached, with the arm he'd kept free, to his belt.
His head was engulfed by the octopus limbs,
And he couldn't look down at the pouch which he felt.
The octopus sensed sudden danger – in fear
It reached for the arm, thus releasing its grip.
The fisherman rolled back in fresh clouds of silt
Pushing hard with his feet as the creature let slip.

He rapidly opened the pouch on his belt,
And his fingers took hold of the contents within.
He pulled out his hand, with the fingers clenched tight,
As the octopus pushed off and started to swim.
One pulse with its legs, and it shot fast ahead –
Like a deadly torpedo it sped at the man.
The fisherman waited until the last moment . . .
Then lunged and released what he held, from his hand.

The thing which he threw was a glittering jewel.
Betrayal had long ago paid for this gem:
'Twas the last of the treasure he'd once had as payment:
A ruby as red as the blood of his friends.
"You once gave me this," thought the captain, "and now
It becomes my defence in this time of attack.
The burden of guilt which came with it remains.
It's that burden I hurl at you! Here! Have it back!"

The octopus, struck, stopped at once in its flight
Sinking down to the deck, trailing limbs as if dead.
The blow of the guilt struck as hard as a hammer:
It suddenly knew where its actions had led.
It felt all the sorrow the villagers felt.
It could feel all the pain: knew the Spaniards' tears.
Far worse, though, the terrible anguish and pain
Which the fisherman carried for two thousand years.

A fizzing of bubbles rose up round its body –
Consumed by the conflict of guilt, hate and love.
The water around boiled and belched bursting bubbles
Which soared to the sea's shining surface above.
The fisherman watched this with deepening sadness.
The centuries taught him one thing through and through:
No matter their actions, you don't hate the *men*:
You must love them, although you might hate what they *do*.

He swam to the chest, seized a handful of coins,
Watched them trickle and spin to the decking below:
A secret supply for the poor and the sick
Of which all local people would very soon know.
He'd long since made plans for the way they'd be given:
The needy, at night, would abandon their pride
And would pin a note pleading their case for some silver
Upon the oak door of the old pub, "McBride".

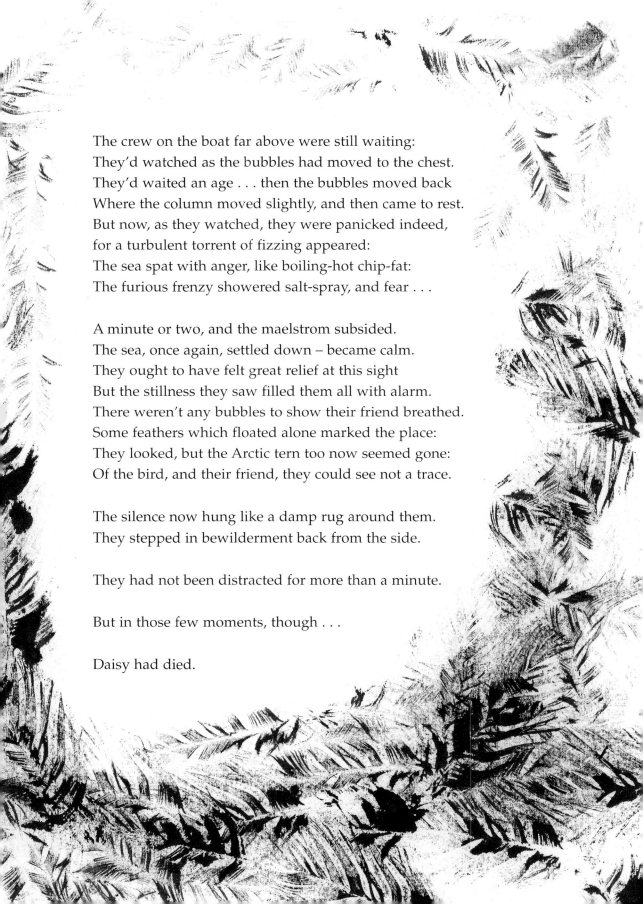

The crew on the boat far above were still waiting:
They'd watched as the bubbles had moved to the chest.
They'd waited an age . . . then the bubbles moved back
Where the column moved slightly, and then came to rest.
But now, as they watched, they were panicked indeed,
for a turbulent torrent of fizzing appeared:
The sea spat with anger, like boiling-hot chip-fat:
The furious frenzy showered salt-spray, and fear . . .

A minute or two, and the maelstrom subsided.
The sea, once again, settled down – became calm.
They ought to have felt great relief at this sight
But the stillness they saw filled them all with alarm.
There weren't any bubbles to show their friend breathed.
Some feathers which floated alone marked the place:
They looked, but the Arctic tern too now seemed gone:
Of the bird, and their friend, they could see not a trace.

The silence now hung like a damp rug around them.
They stepped in bewilderment back from the side.

They had not been distracted for more than a minute.

But in those few moments, though . . .

Daisy had died.

V
RELEASE

NOW, TO HUNTER it seemed that the death of old Daisy
Could not be coincidence. She'd not have gone
Had she not known her master was leaving for good.
The fisherman! No! he'd been down far too long!
In seconds, he'd climbed to the top of the cabin,
Was frantically scanning the sea all around:
The fisherman might not have come to the surface,
But, surely, some sign of him yet would be found?

He strained in the glare of the sun as it settled,
A bright orange ball quenched in sea off Rame Head.
There was no sign of life, not a ripple in sight
And he knew, in his bones, that their friend must be dead.
Nonetheless, they must hunt for him, lest he be trapped
In the rigging and sails, or perhaps in the nets
Which had snagged on the timbers and been left behind
And now hung like a shroud from the sides of the wreck.

He ordered his colleagues to ready themselves
And he told them which tools they should each bring along:
A knife for the netting. A spare air supply.
A torch, for the sun had now very near gone.
With daylight receding, they dropped from the boat,
And together descended the shot line they'd laid.
Their torch beam struck down through the quickening gloom
As above, fading sunlight washed warm on the waves.

They descended with speed, for they knew the way well
Yet the ship, when they reached her, was not as before.
Bright timbers were rotten. The sails were all holed.
Now no clang of a bell, but the creak of a door
As it swung from one hinge from a barnacled cabin.
A mass of thick weed trailed like hair from the mast.
They could see her grow old right in front of their eyes
As if they were watching as centuries passed.

A creak and a groan, and the mast slowly toppled
And fell to one side in a cloud of grey silt.
The wreck, so it seemed, was collapsing around them.
The decks had already developed a tilt.
There wasn't a moment to waste! Hunter swam
Past the wheel-house and bell till he came to the place
Where the chest had once sat, but the light from his torch
Showed him nothing. Of treasure, there wasn't a trace.

From the shadows nearby, though, his torch beam struck steel
And he swam quickly onwards to see what was there:
The fisherman's weight belt, his knife and his valve
Were laid out by his bottle, now empty of air.
He'd never before left a bottle unfinished
And other things, too, he had done in his way:
For there, with the sleeves neatly folded across it,
The fisherman's jacket, they noticed, now lay.

Their own air supply had now fallen so low
That they knew they should surface at once if they could.
They couldn't delay any longer, and turned
And swam swiftly through tangles of fast-rotting wood.
They searched for the spot where the shotline had been,
And then found the right place – yes, of that they were sure –
But the shotline was no longer there to be found
And the anchor had gone from the rocky sea floor.

They panicked, and headed at once for the top
Swimming up in the welter of bubbles they'd made.
They burst into air, ripped their masks from their heads,
Spat their valves from their mouths, ditched their tanks to the waves.
And the boat which they'd dived from was no longer there!
She had sailed, so it seemed, on her own out to sea
Having pulled up her anchor, and started her engines . . .
But that, they all knew, couldn't possibly be . . .

Nonetheless, as the sun yielded gently to moonlight
And Hunter was wiping salt spray from his eyes
He thought that perhaps he could see, silhouetted,
The shape of a boat as it crossed the dark skies.
And he'd swear that he made out a treasure chest's shape
With a man in the bow, and that there by his side
Was a dog looking happily up at her master
United once more on the wind and the tide . . .

If it hadn't been dark and they hadn't now started
To swim as a group for the silvery shore,
He might then have seen that the ship had been joined
By some friends who were sailing a dozen ships more . . .

The crew and their wives woke next day to the feeling
That something around them was not as it seemed.
They'd slept like the dead, but strange visions of treasure
And captains called 'Bruno' had come in their dreams.
Not one of them now could remember the time
That they'd spent on the ship in those last seven days,
For their memories all were erased by the dawn,
Like a mist which dispersed in the sun's warming rays.

They packed with the thought that they'd merely been tourists.
With that in their minds, they all made their way home
With no memory now of the friends they had made
And convinced that they'd spent all their time on their own.
Steve Hunter went on to become a great surgeon,
And happily lived with his good wife, Louise.
He never once thought of a different career
As an Admiral sailing the world's stormy seas . . .

Up near Oxford, Chris Edge and his lovely wife Jenny
With young Alexandra, Victoria too,
Lived happily – he with his medical work,
And she with her silversmith's work still to do.
She also devoted much time to the care
Of her special collection of old Bonsai trees.
Chris never did think he might save a king's life
As a doctor who sailed on the world's stormy seas . . .

As for Adrian . . . well . . . that's a mystery still
And we never shall know what he knew then (or knows)
For a year or so later he moved down to Plymouth
With Bridget, and Jack, and young Patrick in tow.
On arriving, he found himself work in a pub
And of their new barman, the locals all swore
That he took to the job in the old pub "McBride"
In a way which suggested he'd done it before . . .

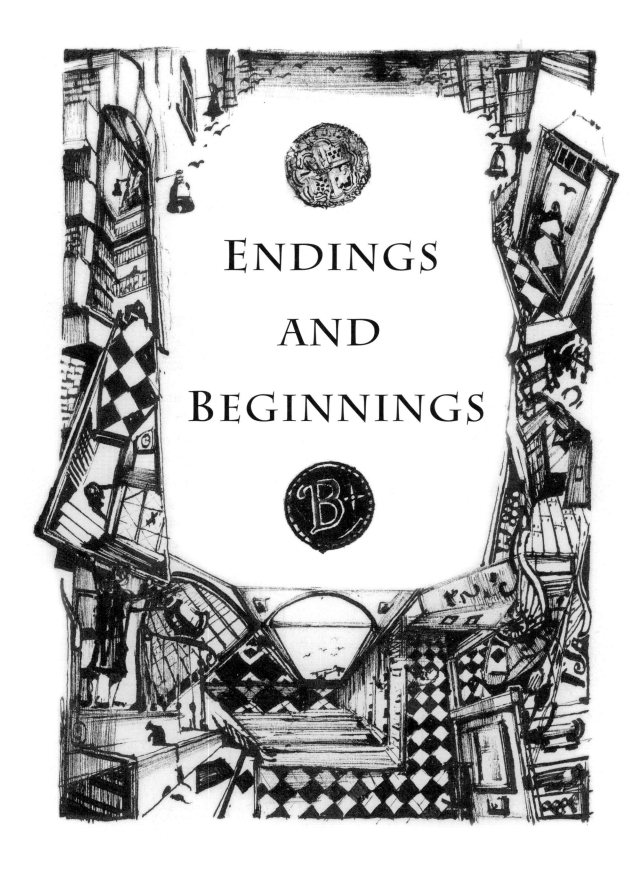

ENDINGS

AND

BEGINNINGS

I
THREE TALES?

SO NOW I've finished. You have heard
Three separate stories. One occurred
In Northern parts: an evil man
Set out to conquer other lands.
A local village was betrayed
By some poor fisherman he paid
To sell his friends. Each of them died
And only this one man survived.

The second tale was set in Spain.
I won't repeat it all again,
For you will know how Bruno went
To seek a peaceful settlement
With Spain, and how he saved the king
From certain death from poisoning,
And how the traitor's boat was lost
In Heybrook Bay, near Renne's Rocks.

The final tale, as now you know,
Was set just thirty years ago.
The traitor's boat was found once more
Upon the rocky ocean floor
Unchanged by all the centuries
She'd spent beneath the Devon seas.
The treasure still lay on the ship.
An octopus was guarding it.

But what connects these times of old?
And what connects the tales I've told?
Foul betrayal, certainly
Occurs in two tales of the three.
But could it be that evil deeds
Can never in the end succeed
And, for this reason, that we find
All wrongs are righted, given time?

So, was the man in Northern climes,
Who sailed the seas in olden times,
And took the jewels and sold his friends,
The same man who then made amends
For all his selfishness and greed,
By helping in his hour of need
Lord Hunter, who might yet have drowned
Unless (by chance?) he'd first been found?

And was he, by Lord Hunter, asked
To sail with him to foreign parts
And did he then proceed to save
The Spanish king, who'd been betrayed?
And was this man the same as he
Who later went beneath the sea
And made a living raising scrap
By diving down with ropes and sacks?

And did he sail through centuries
On Northern and on local seas
In just one boat? Did he arrive
In waters down near Bretonside
Aboard the good ship *Arctic Tern*?
Was this the same boat which you learned
Was sailed to Spain, and from whose decks
The divers later sought the wreck?

And were that howling hairy man
Who'd also lived in Northern lands,
For whom plain evil was the goal
(Who bought, in jewels, the very soul
Of that poor man aboard his boat
And paid him to betray his folks),
And 'Mad Dog' just one and the same?
Did *he* betray the King of Spain?

And finally, you must decide
If all the sailors I've described
(Like Doctor Chris and Adrian
And Hunter) were the self-same men
Who sailed with Bruno first to Spain:
And did they really come again
When, lifetimes later, Bruno asked
His friends to help him in his task?

Perhaps the debts are fully paid,
And Bruno saved a man betrayed
– A token act to make amends
In part for having killed his friends.
And having caused great pain before,
Perhaps he tried to aid the poor
And help those folks of failing health
By giving them enormous wealth
Which, with his friends, he later found
Upon that wreck in Plymouth Sound.

The jesters sometimes make their way
Past Wembury beach to Heybrook Bay,
And in these places sift the sands
With patience, through their gentle hands,
In hope of finding on the shore
Some scraps of silver washed ashore:
Return, though, laughing if the beach
Has kept its treasure out of reach.

And if you take a stroll one day,
You too can walk to Heybrook Bay.
But if you search all day and find
No more than shells, then never mind:
It's not just fools, but wise men too
Who know to value what is true:
The warmth of friendship — that's the best,
Worth more than any treasure chest.

II
TODAY

SO NOW you've listened to my tale
Of Bruno, and of how he sailed
With friends aboard *The Arctic Tern*:
I hope you'll treasure what you've learned.
And one day you might think of it
And go to Plymouth, see the ships
And all the places I've described:
The pub ("The Admiral McBride"),
The drinking trough, and Wembury beach,
And Heybrook Bay, are all in reach,
And other sites are close at hand
Like Cap'n Jasper's burger stand.

You might then go to Wembury beach
And, at low tide, you there might seek
The jewels the fisherman threw down
Where waves roll in from Plymouth Sound.
Occasionally, a searching hand
Which gently sifts the seashore sand
Will find some item thought to be
No more than glass washed by the sea.
Such coloured pieces (red and green)
May not in fact be what they seem
And may in fact be something more
Than broken bottle on the shore.

At Heybrook Bay one sometimes spots
Some wooden fragments on the rocks.
Amongst them, some old bits are found
Whose weathered surfaces are browned
And worn and ragged. Parts like these
Have surfaced from beneath the seas.
From wrecks long lost, and some may float
Towards the shore from Mad Dog's boat
Which lies not very far at all
From Renne's Rocks, you will recall.

At night-time, you might also hear
A dog which barks. Well, never fear:
They say that Daisy walks around
At nightfall in the darkened town
As she re-visits all the sites
That she remembers, and by night
Will make her way towards the docks,
Or walk the shore near Renne's Rocks.
If at the Barbican one day
You catch a glimpse of some poor stray,
Then show some kindness to the hound –
It might be Daisy that you've found.

III
REPRISE

IN DEVON LIES the Naval Town of Plymouth,
The home of submarines and ships of war,
Of frigates, battleships and pleasure cruisers,
Of ferries, cargo boats and many more.
In summer, tourists throng along the sea front
Or splash along the beach at Bovisand
Or climb the Mayflower steps where Pilgrim Fathers
Set sail to colonise a foreign land.

But when you visit, try to look about you,
Beyond the burgers, ice-cream and the trips:
Imagine what this place might once have looked like
When Plymouth Sound was full of wooden ships.
The ancient port would then be full of dangers:
Of vagabonds and smugglers – pirates too,
And simply walking out alone one evening
Could find you coming round as press-ganged crew.

Perhaps you'll come to natter to a sailor –
An old man who will tell you all the tales
Of local crooks and privateers and pirates:
The gold and silver carried as they sailed.
Perhaps he'll speak of caves crammed full with diamonds,
Of treasure chests long buried out of reach,
Of times when customs men and smugglers battled
And pearls and blood were spilled at Wembury beach.

But there's one tale I know that he won't mention:
Of Bruno and his quest for Spanish gold.
And of the little boat which he had captained
I guarantee you'll never hear a word.
Things happen here in Plymouth in the winter
And of such things you'd surely never learn.
So take your seat and listen while I tell you
Of Bruno and his ship, *The Arctic Tern* . . .

All life is quenched. But let this be a setting sun,
Its fire in balm embalmed. Its flame not snuffed, but soothed at sleep
With one last whisper of warm breath.

Yet radiant – remains, suspended still in memory
Will brush with buttered gold the souls of those still left who weep.
The poor, enriched by noble death.

Acknowledgements

I should like to thank the crew – whether volunteer or press-ganged. Thanks to Bruno, Clare McClintock, Seana Smith and to Margaret Rule and the Mary Rose Diving Team, for many happy memories of diving days: to Clare Dollery, who became an ill-tempered parrot: and to the Hunter, Edge, Gardner and Naunton-Morgan families: to Nick Poullis, Mónica Bratt and Miriam Richardson for believing when others had less faith. Especial thanks to Mary, who was widowed by this book and without whom it would never have been written, and to Andrew Gardner whom I miss very much. He represented honesty and the best of journalism. Finally, if there are noble views espoused in this book, these belong to my parents. They have devoted their lives to their children, and to the children of others. My love and respect to them.